Introduction to Error-Correcting Codes

For a complete listing of the *Artech House Telecommunications Library*,
turn to the back of this book

Introduction to Error-Correcting Codes

Michael Purser

Artech House
Boston • London

Library of Congress Cataloging-in-Publication Data
Purser, Michael, 1937-
Introduction to error-correcting codes
Includes bibliographical references and index.
ISBN 0-89006-784-8
1. Signal processing. 2. Error-correcting codes (Information theory) I. Title
TK5102.9.P87   1995   94-32112
621.382'2–dc20   CIP

British Library Cataloguing in Publication Data
Purser, Michael
Introduction to Error-correcting Codes
I. Title
621-382

ISBN 0-89006-784-8

© 1995 ARTECH HOUSE, INC.
685 Canton Street
Norwood, MA 02062

International Standard Book Number: 0-89006-784-8
Library of Congress Catalog Card Number: 94-32112

10 9 8 7 6 5 4 3 2

Contents

Preface   v

Chapter 1   Introduction   1
  1.1   Bit Strings ond Codes   1
    1.1.1   Codes and Error Correction   3
    1.1.2   Erasures and Soft-Decision Decoding   5
  1.2   Hamming Distance and Sphere-Packing   7
  1.3   Shannon's Theorem   8

Chapter 2   Linear Codes   11
  2.1   Matrix Representation   11
    2.1.1   The Standard Array   12
    2.1.2   The Generator Matrix   13
  2.2   The Null Matrix or Parity-Check Matrix   14
    2.2.1   The Syndrome   15
    2.2.2   The Columns of the Null Matrix   17
  2.3   Perfect Codes   18
  2.4   Further Bounds on Linear Codes   19
    2.4.1   The Varsharmov-Gilbert Bound   19
    2.4.2   The Plotkin Bound   20
    2.4.3   Bounds in Practice   23
  2.5   Nonbinary Linear Codes   25
    2.5.1   Nonbinary Codes with Characteristic 2   28

Chapter 3   Cyclic Codes   31
  3.1   The Generating Polynomial   31
    3.1.1   Systematic Cyclic Codes   33
  3.2   The Roots of $g(x)$ and the Null Matrix   35

3.3   Error Detection with Cyclic Codes   38
      3.3.1   Weight Distributions   39
      3.3.2   Shortened Cyclic Codes and Feedback Shift Registers   40
3.4   Error Correction with Cyclic Codes   42
3.5   Nonbinary Cyclic Codes   44

Chapter 4   BCH Codes   47
4.1   Minimum Polynomials   47
4.2   The Roots of BCH Codes   48
4.3   Some Examples of BCH Codes   51
4.4   Error Correction of Binary BCH Codes   53
      4.4.1   Practical Procedures for Solving the Equations   54
      4.4.2   An Example of BCH Error Correction   56
4.5   Error Correction of Nonbinary BCH Codes   58
4.6   Reed-Solomon (RS) Codes   59
      4.6.1   A Worked RS Example   60
      4.6.2   An Example of Practical Use of RS Codes   62
      4.6.3   Other Aspects of RS Codes   64

Chapter 5   Convolutional Codes   69
5.1   Tree and Trellis Codes   69
      5.1.1   The Viterbi Algorithm   70
5.2   Linear Convolutional Codes   72
      5.2.1   Control of Decoding Errors   77
5.3   Analysis of Convolutional Codes   78
5.4   Error-Correcting with Convolutional Codes   81
      5.4.1   Soft-Decision Decoding   84
      5.4.2   Sequential Decoding   85
      5.4.3   Feedback Decoding   86
      5.4.4   Syndrome Decoding: A Worked Example   89
5.5   Block Codes and Convolutional Codes   91

Appendix A   Information Theory   95

Appendix B   Some Binomial Approximations   113

Appendix C   Finite Fields   117

Appendix D   The Berlekamp-Massey Algorithm   125

References   129

Index   131

Preface

This book aims to be an introduction to the topic of error-correcting codes, a topic of major importance in digital communication whenever accuracy is critical.

There are several excellent specialist textbooks (and one or two almost unreadable ones) on the subject, in addition to innumerable articles and papers in the journals. Despite this, the basics of digital error detection and correction are unfamiliar to many who might easily understand them, even when they rely on those techniques in much of their professional work. In the author's opinion this situation arises from the lack of clear, concise introductory texts on the subject; and it is his hope that this book will be such a text.

There are at least three good reasons for studying the subject:

- It is an ingenious and intellectually satisfying discipline in its own right
- It is an application of branches of mathematics, notably that of finite fields, that gives stimulus to the study of those branches
- It is a technology of immense practical use in computer and telecommunication systems

This book aims to illuminate all three of these aspects and, by presenting basic concepts and results, give the reader a firm grasp of the scope of the subject and a thorough understanding of the principal techniques. On this basis the reader should be able to pursue any future interest in more specialised areas of the subject without difficulty. There are many such areas.

The intended readership is the first-time student, whether one who is formally studying in a third-level institution or a computer or communications professional wishing to become familiar with the subject by self-education. Mathematical literacy is required, in particular familiarity with linear algebra, but no further exceptional ability or special knowledge is needed.

The course of the book moves from the general concepts of block codes and distances (Chapter 1), through linear block codes (Chapter 2), to the special linear codes that are cyclic codes (Chapter 3) and the special cyclic codes that are BCH codes (Chapter 4).

By contrast Chapter 5 is devoted to Convolutional or Trellis Codes, in which data are in the form of an "infinite" stream, rather than a fixed-length block. Supporting mathematics is in the Appendices, so that those readers already familiar with, for example, finite fields can proceed through the main text directly.

The author hopes indeed that his aim of a clear, concise introduction has been achieved. It remains his pleasure to thank his professional colleagues in the computer industry and his students at Trinity College in Dublin who helped to stimulate his interest in error correction and who inspired this book. Special thanks are due to Jennifer O'Reilly, who typed it.

Chapter 1
Introduction

1.1 BIT STRINGS AND CODES

In computers and in digital telecommunications information is almost always represented in binary form, that is, as a sequence of bits each having the value 0 or 1. In its original form the information may have a different representation. It could be text represented as words and punctuation based on an alphabet; it could be speech or video represented as analogue signals. But whatever the original or intermediate form, the final representation is binary. The alphabet is turned into 6-, 7-, or 8-bit patterns; the speech and video are sampled, quantised, and digitised.

A sequence of bits may be of any length. For example, digitised TV signals provide a continuous, virtually endless bit-stream. Alternatively the sequence may divide naturally into units such as octets or bytes representing the characters in an alphabet. For practical reasons, sequences of bits are also frequently divided into blocks that may have little relation to the structure of the content of the information. This is done to facilitate handling; a typical example is the blocking of a bit-stream into "packets" of fixed maximum length (e.g., 256 octets) for transmission over a packet-switched network.

In this book we are concerned with detecting and correcting errors that typically occur when such sequences of bits are transmitted over communication channels. It is worthwhile considering for a moment why one should want to do so, or at least, why one should want to employ the relatively complex and sophisticated techniques that have been developed for error correction. After all, a large proportion of distorted information is readily corrected by the human eye, ear, and brain, without any other aids. One need only consider reading a letter from someone who cannot spell, or a newspaper, or a corrupted fax message; listening to an incoherent child or to someone with a speech impediment; or watching a badly tuned TV set, to realise how great one's capabilities are for recreating sense from apparent nonsense.

But the essence of this ability to correct errors is that we make use of *redundancy* in the information. One or two key words in a garbled message enable us to guess the rest because the rest was hardly necessary in the first place. A Spaniard can read an Italian newspaper without knowing Italian, because he recognises the stems of a few basic nouns and verbs. Most of the rest of the written text is superfluous to him. Redundancy, often huge redundancy, exists in almost all information. Consider, for example, ordinary text. There is redundancy

- In the orthography. For example, in English the U following a Q is quite unnecessary. More drastically, it is possible to leave out most vowels from written English and to reduce all double letters to single ones and still leave the text intelligible.
- In the syntax. For example, definite and indefinite articles in English can often be omitted harmlessly; in languages in which the verbs are inflected the personal pronoun is usually superfluous.
- In the semantics. "At this moment in time" can be cut down to "At this moment" or "At this time" or indeed discarded in favour of "now."

(We do not consider complete redundancy in which the message is, for example, a repetition of what we know already or perhaps just irrelevant.)

But some information is less redundant and more compact than other information. It is usually impossible to remove a single instruction or parameter from a computer program in machine language without destroying the program's meaning, at least to the computer that interprets it, if not to a skilled and critical programmer reading it.

From certain viewpoints redundancy is a weakness. It is a waste of space. In particular it is a waste of capacity on communication channels, which are often bottlenecks in computer systems if redundant information is transmitted. Many compression techniques exist for removing redundancy from text and other data streams; in the case of voice and video these techniques are complex and clever and compress raw digital signals by factors of 10, or 100, or even more.

A second way of looking at redundancy reveals another associated weakness. Essentially redundancy means that out of all possible strings of characters (e.g., in a text) only a small proportion are valid. Thus, a Q in English not followed by a U is invalid, and a message containing such a Q is not possible in the normally written language. This aspect is explored marvellously in Jorge Luis Borges' "La Biblioteca" ("The Library"), which contains all combinations of letters and texts possible, and hence contains (in all languages) all knowledge, including, for example, the future history of the world. The problem is to find the text you are looking for. If you do find it, is it true? Another text, if you could find it, would tell you if it is or not (correctly or not?). Perhaps the searching procedure could be simplified by looking up the catalogue, which must be in the library-if you could find it. This fantasy conceals an important truth, namely, that in searching for hidden information you use redundancy to distinguish sense from nonsense. In practical terms if you know the process by which secret text is encrypted and decrypted without knowing the specific key, trying out all possible keys may enable you to find the correct one (and hence the secret message) by testing if the cyphertext decrypted with the test key value makes sense or not. Shannon has shown that if the key length used in encryption is shorter than the length of the "information contents" of the secret message this "attack" has a high probability of success. That is, a trial-and-error attack using all possible keys for decryption will yield only *one meaningful message* the correct one. The concepts of "information content" and "redundancy" as originated by Shannon, the founder of Information Theory, are explored in more detail in Appendix A [1, 2].

From the point of view of error detection and correction, the custom of removing redundancy from information either to compress it or to foil "try-all-the-keys" decryption is a serious problem. Without redundancy one message is as valid as another, so the corruption of one message necessarily produces another valid one; and since the recipient has no means of knowing that it has been corrupted, the error goes undetected. But even with redundancy that enables the occurrence of an error to be detected by the nonsense that results on re-expanding the compressed or decrypting the garbled encrypted message, we may be quite unable to recreate the original data. That is because the complexity of the expansion and decryption process is likely to spread errors in a small part of the transmitted data to such an extent that a large part of, if not all the processed data are corrupted. The error is detected but cannot be corrected. A good example of this spreading of an error can be seen on many fax machines, which use compression, and where one or two bit errors may destroy a whole scan line.

1.1.1 Codes and Error Correction

It is the central function of error-control techniques to reintroduce controlled redundancy, which will overcome these problems, by enabling messages corrupted in transmission to be corrected before further processing. With this controlled redundancy only a subset of all possible transmitted messages (bit sequences) contains valid messages. The subset is then called a code, and the valid messages are called *codewords* or *codevectors*. A good code is one in which the codewords are so "separated" that the likelihood of errors corrupting one into another is kept small.

Error detection then is simplified to answering this question: Is the received message a codeword or not? If it is a codeword, one assumes that no errors have occurred. The probability of an undetected error getting through is then the probability of sufficient errors occurring to transform the real transmitted codeword into another, apparently correct but in reality a false one.

If an error is detected, it can be corrected in principle by one of two methods:

- The recipient rejects the received message as erroneous and requests the original transmitter for a repeat transmission (see Figure 1.1). This recovery by retransmission is commonplace in communication systems where it is possible. However, if propagation delays, due to distance, are large, the technique may become so inefficient as to be useless. And then there are other cases where retransmission is not possible, for example, if one considers a corrupted archive without a backup.
- The recipient corrects the errors by finding the valid codeword "nearest" to the received message, on the assumption that the nearest is the most likely, because few corrupting errors are more likely than many! This procedure is often called forward error correction (FEC) and is one of the principal topics of this book. See Figure 1.2.

As an example of these ideas, consider the digits 0 and 1 extended to 3 bits in

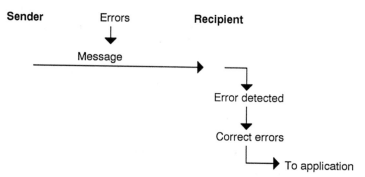

Figure 1.1 Error-recovery by detection and retransmission.

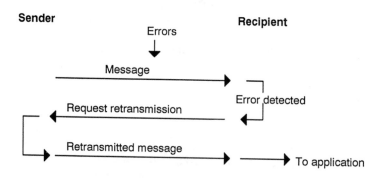

Figure 1.2 Forward error correction (FEC).

length, using 2 redundant bits, to become 010 and 101 respectively. These are then the only two valid codewords of 3 bits in length; if one receives 000, 001, 011, 100, 110, or 111, one has detected an error.

These invalid vectors can be associated with the valid ones to facilitate error correction; thus,

010	101
011	001
110	100
000	111

where we have placed in the column beneath each codeword those 3-bit patterns that differ from it by only one bit the "nearest" ones. If we receive 011, for example, we know it is invalid, but we correct it by saying that it most likely is a corruption of 010, representing 0. It could, however, be 101, with the first *two* bits corrupted, in that case we would have made the error worse by our so-called correction, but this is a less likely event.

Why is it less likely? The assumption here is that the probability of a bit being corrupted, p, is small, so that the probability of one error in three, $p(1-p)^2$, is significantly greater than the probability of two errors in three, $p^2(1-p)$. If $p = 0.1$, for example, $p(1-p)^2 = 0.081$, whereas $p^2(1-p) = 0.009$ (p is necessarily less than or equal to 0.5. If it were greater, we would simply complement the entire bit string and then work with $(1-p)$.)

Obviously an FEC technique that relies on comparing the received message with all codewords to find the nearest one is impracticable for long codes with many codewords. For example, many codes will have 2^{1000} or 2^{2000} codewords. Such codes are not a more-or-less random collection of reasonably well separated vectors (as one might be tempted to choose), but rather a carefully structured set with a complex internal consistency. Error correction then exploits this structure and consistency to find the codeword nearest to the received vector, using mathematics.

1.1.2 Erasures and Soft-Decision Decoding

We finish this introduction by pointing out that so far we have assumed that the recipient has been presented with a corrupted received message or vector with no further information as to the nature and location of the errors. We have also assumed that the errors, insofar as they affect individual bits, are random and uniform over all bits. Neither of these assumptions is necessarily true.

In many systems the bits received are the result of some prior processing, such as demodulation of an analogue waveform, or at least a threshold detector that decides whether a level is nearer 0 or 1. This preprocessor may qualify the bit values it produces, and this additional information can be used to improve further the error-correcting procedures. For example, some bits could be flagged as "uncertain", that is, either 0 or 1, and could be omitted in the search for the nearest codeword and filled in only after the codeword was found. A channel that gives this 3-valued output (0, 1, X = uncertain) is called a Binary Erasure Channel. To see how an Erasure Channel permits more accurate decoding compared with a "hard-decision" channel, consider the previous 3-bit example and suppose we receive 0X1. If we had been told that this was 001, we would have said 101 was transmitted; if we had been told that it was 011, we would have said 010 was transmitted. But if we work with 0X1, we compare with 0X0 and 1X1, from which 0X1 is equidistant and conclude that we do not know what was transmitted. This is certainly more accurate (if less conclusive) than "hard-decoding" based on a prior, possibly arbitrary decision by a preprocessor, of which we are ignorant.

The Erasure Channel is a special example of a more general channel that delivers qualifying information for each bit, for example, some sort of *reliability* factor. These reliability factors can be used to influence the concept and evaluation of "nearness". Thus, each bit might have an accompanying factor of value 0.5 to 1.0, which would be the estimated probability that it is what it claims to be. If we receive 0(0.5), 1(0.6), 1(0.9), where the value in parentheses are the probabilities, then we could say the "distance" to 010 is $0.5 + 0.4 + 0.9 = 1.8$, whereas the "distance" to 101 is $0.5 + 0.6 + 0.1 = 1.2$, and we would decode the received 011 to 101, *not* to 010. (Alternatively we could say that the probability of 010 given the received values is $0.5 \cdot 0.6 \cdot 0.1 = 0.03$, whereas the probability of 101 is $0.5 \cdot 0.4 \cdot 0.9 = 0.18$ and again choose 101 in preference to 010). This sort of decoding technique, in which reliability factors are taken into account, is called "soft-decision decoding". It has useful applications, particularly in delicate systems, but in many cases it is simply not practicable, because the receiver of the data is presented with an uncompromising and unqualified bit stream by other equipment over which he has little or no control.

The other assumption that has been implicit in this introduction is that bit errors are random and uniform. In practice this is seldom so. Errors have their causes, and if that cause is an electrical "spike", a momentary short-circuit, or a scratch on a magnetic medium, it is common that the corruption affects more than one bit. This will happen if the "noise" lasts for longer than a bit-time or spreads wider than a bit-space on the medium. *Bursts* of errors are created, usually at widely spaced, irregular intervals. Error-correction techniques take account of burst-errors in various ways, such as

- Rearranging the sequence of the data so that the burst of errors is scattered randomly throughout it;
- Using specifically designed burst-error-detecting and-correcting codes (e.g., Fire codes);

- Handling groups of bits, rather than individual bits, as the basic code symbols, so that a short burst of single-bit errors becomes one symbol error (e.g., Reed-Solomon codes).

1.2 HAMMING DISTANCE AND SPHERE-PACKING

Following on from the above heuristic introduction, we may now try to be somewhat more precise.

We consider *block codes*. A block code is defined as a subset of all the possible 2^n binary vectors having n bits in length. The distance, also called the Hamming distance in honour of R.W. Hamming, between two such vectors is defined as the number of bit positions at which the two vectors have differing values [3]. The distance of the code, the *code-distance*, is defined as the minimum distance between any two members of the code, that is, between any two code-words.

The first aim in designing a good code is to ensure that its distance is as large as possible, so as to enable as many errors as possible to be corrected. If the distance $d = 2t + 1$, it is clear that we can *detect* all corruptions that affect $\leq 2t$ bits of a codeword, because they can never transform one codeword into another. It is also clear that we can, at least in principle, *correct* all corruptions affecting $\leq t$ bits of a codeword, because the corrupted word will be nearer (i.e., have a smaller distance) to the original codeword than to any other. If d is even, $d = 2t$, we can detect $(2t - 1)$ errors; but we can correct only $(t - 1)$ errors, because t errors could bring us as near to some other codeword as to the original one. (As an example, if 00 and 11 are codewords with $n = 2$, we can detect 01 and 10 as errors but we cannot correct them).

The second aim in good code design is to construct the code, that is, select the subset from all possible 2^n vectors, in such a way that error detection and correction can be performed without the need to compare the received vector with all valid codewords.

Returning to the problem of maximising the distance of the code, it is obvious that the number of codewords in the code is the principal restriction on our liberty. If there exist M codewords, we can imagine each codeword surrounded by a "sphere" of related vectors, nearer to it than to any other codeword, comprising the codeword corrupted by all single-bit errors, all two-bit errors, and so on, up to all t-bit vectors. The number of such related vectors is $S(n, t)$, and

$$S(n,t) = \binom{n}{1} + \binom{n}{2} + \binom{n}{3} + \cdots + \binom{n}{t}$$

where the parentheses are binomial coefficients. If we include the original codeword itself, then each sphere contains $(1 + S(n, t))$ vectors. To respect the distance $d = 2t + 1$ of the code, these spheres cannot overlap; therefore,

$$M(1 + S(n, t)) \leq 2^n \tag{1.1}$$

This is a necessary condition for a code of distance d; but not sufficient.

In Appendix B it is shown that for large $n, t = \alpha n$, and $\alpha < 1/2, 1 + S(n, t) \leq 2^{nH(\alpha)}$, where $H(\alpha)$ is the entropy function.

$$H(\alpha) = -(\alpha \log_2 \alpha + (1 - \alpha)\log_2(1 - \alpha)).$$

Thus, if

$$M \leq 2^{n[1 - H(\alpha)]} \tag{1.2}$$

is satisfied, (1.1) is certainly satisfied, so we may use (1.2) for large n. For example, if $n = 8, t = 2$ (so that we have a two-error correcting code, if we can find one), using inequality (1.1) we get $M(1 + 8 + 28) \leq 256$, so $M \leq 6.9$.

The codevectors could be 00000000, 01111100, 10011111, and 11100011, but we have found only four, not six. The code's (minimum) distance $= 2t + 1 = 5$; the distance between the second and fourth codewords and the first and third is 6, and this explains why M is smaller than expected.

Inequality (1.2) is known as the *sphere-packing bound*. If we take logarithms to the base 2 in (1.2), we have

$$\log_2 M \leq n(1 - H(\alpha)) \tag{1.3}$$

This states that for large n, the effective length of the code, from the point of view of the number of unrestricted information bits we can put into a codeword (the remaining bits being redundant, but used for error detection and correction) is bounded by $n(1 - H(\alpha))$, with $a = t/n$.

A code that is composed of k information bits, which can have 2^k arbitrary values, and $(n - k)$ redundant bits or *check digits* is called a systematic (n, k) code. Our example is a systematic $(8, 2)$ code with the first two bits being the information bits. Inequality (1.3) states that $k/n \leq 1 - H(\alpha)$, where $\alpha = t/n = (d - 1)/2n$. k/n is known as the *code rate*. Note that, in (1.1), in the special case when n is odd and $t = (n - 1)/2$ we have $(1 + S(n, t)) = 2^{n-1}$; so that $M \leq 2$. The two codewords are then $000\ldots00$ and $111\ldots11$.

1.3 SHANNON'S THEOREM

Inequality (1.2) puts an upper limit on the number of codewords that can exist if a minimum distance $d = 2t + 1$ is to be attained. But we have seen even in our simple example that there may be difficulties in finding a code with M approaching the limit. Do such codes exist?

Shannon addressed this question obliquely by considering the problem of correctly decoding a corrupted codeword [4]. His decoding rule is

If the probability of a bit error is p, then search in the sphere around **r**, the received vector, using a radius $n(p + \varepsilon)$, where ε is very small, for a codeword. If a single one is found, decode **r** to it. If none is found, or if two or more are found, decoding fails.

Thus, $(p + \varepsilon)$ corresponds to our α, but the sphere is centred on **r**, not on a codeword.

With this method

$$P_E = \text{Prob(Decoding failure)} = \text{Prob(No codeword)}$$
$$+ \text{Prob(Two or more codewords)}$$

For large n, Prob(No codeword) $< \delta$, where δ is an arbitrary small constant, because the expected distance of the original uncorrupted codeword from **r** is np, with standard deviation proportional to $(np)^{1/2}$. As n increases, this is bound to be less than $n(p + \varepsilon)$. Note that δ is independent of the choice of code itself and of the particular vector received.

The probability of two or more codewords being found in the sphere surrounding the received vector clearly depends on the code used and on that vector. However, if we average over all possible codes having M codewords and also possible received vectors, we get

$$\text{Prob(2 or more codewords)} = (M - 1)(1/2^n)\left(\binom{n}{1} + \binom{n}{2} + \cdots + \binom{n}{qn}\right)$$

where $q = (p + \varepsilon)$

This is the proportion of the $(M - 1)$ remaining codewords, using the ratio of the number of vectors in the "sphere" to the total number. Replacing $(M - 1)$ with M and using the inequality of Appendix B, we get

$$\text{Prob(Two or more codewords)} < M2^{nH(q)}/2^n$$

Accordingly

$$\bar{P}_E < \delta + M/2n^{(1-H(q))}$$

where $\bar{P}_E$ is the average probability of error over all codes and received vectors.

Provided that

$$M < 2^{n(1-H(p))} \tag{1.4}$$

$\bar{P}_E$ can be made arbitrarily small by increasing n and reducing ε.

But if the average error probability over all codes can be made arbitrarily small, then there must exist at least one code that has the same effect, averaged over all possible received vectors. Therefore, P_E can be made arbitrarily small provided that

- A suitable code is chosen.
- n is large enough.
- $M < 2^{n(1-H(p))}$.

Looking back to Inequality (1.2), we see that, if the bit-error probability p is given, we can in theory find a code that will correct all error patterns of $t = pn$ bits or less with arbitrarily small probability of erroneous decoding, with M almost equal to $2^{n(1-H(p))}$. We cannot increase t without being obliged to reduce M, because of Inequality (1.2), and we cannot reduce t to allow M to increase because this would violate Inequality (1.4), and we would begin to suffer erroneous decoding.

In Appendix A it is shown that $(1 - H(p))$ is the *capacity* of a *binary symmetric channel*, in which all bits 0 or 1 are uniformly subject to being complemented with probability p.

$$\text{Capacity} = C = (1 - H(p))$$

Taking logarithms to base 2 in Inequality (1.4) with $M = 2^k$, we get

$$\text{Coderate} = k/n < C$$

This is Shannon's famous theorem, which effectively states that we can achieve virtually error-free communications provided we choose a suitable code (and such a one exists if we can only find it), n is large enough, and the coderate does not exceed the channel's capacity.

Chapter 2
Linear Codes

2.1 MATRIX REPRESENTATION

The first step in imposing some internal structure on a code, which is otherwise an arbitrary collection of M vectors out of 2^n, is to make it *linear*.

In a linear code the n elements of the vector are elements of a finite field, F. Finite fields are presented in Appendix C. For the moment it is sufficient to remember that a finite field is a finite collection of elements, including 0 (additive identity) and 1 (multiplicative identity), between which addition/subtraction and multiplication/division are defined. Each element, α, has an additive inverse, $-\alpha$. Each element, β, except 0 has a multiplicative inverse, β^{-1}. We are concerned at the moment only with the finite field ($GF(2)$) of two elements, 0 and 1. The following properties apply:

$$0 + 0 = 0 \qquad 0 + 1 = 1 + 0 = 1 \qquad 1 + 1 = 0 \text{ (note particularly)}$$

$$0 \times 0 = 0 \qquad 0 \times 1 = 1 \times 0 = 0 \qquad 1 \times 1 = 1$$

For a code to be linear, the following rule applies:
  If c_1 and c_2 are codewords, and α_1, α_2 are field elements, then

$$c = \alpha_1 c_1 + \alpha_2 c_2 \tag{2.1}$$

is a codeword. Equation (2.1) uses the definitions that if $c_1 = (c_{11}, c_{12}, c_{13}, \ldots, c_{1n})$ and similarly for c_2 then addition of vectors is

$$c_1 + c_2 = (c_{11} + c_{21}, c_{12} + c_{22}, \ldots, c_{1n} + c_{2n})$$

and multiplication by a scalar α_1 is $\alpha_1 c_1 = (\alpha_1 c_{11}, \alpha_1 c_{12}, \alpha_1 c_{13} \ldots \alpha_1 c_{1n})$

In common mathematical language, then, a linear code is a *subspace* within the n-dimensional vector space of all n-tuples over a finite field.

2.1.1 The Standard Array

Equation (2.1) effectively defines the subspace by stating that the code is *closed* under addition and scalar multiplication, because if these operations are performed on any codewords we simply produce another codeword. The code is also a *subgroup* of the group of 2^n n-tuples, closed under addition. The code necessarily contains $\mathbf{0} = (0,0\ldots0)$, which we shall usually call $\mathbf{c}_0$, so the codewords may be labelled $\mathbf{c}_0, \mathbf{c}_1, \ldots, \mathbf{c}_{M-1}$. It is important to note that, since the difference between any two codewords is itself a codeword, the minimum distance of the code is the *minimum weight* of the nonzero codewords, where the weight is defined as the number of nonzero bits in a codeword. Since the code is a subgroup, we may construct *cosets* in the usual way to form the *standard array*. The procedure is to write down the codewords in a row,

$$\mathbf{c}_0 \mathbf{c}_1 \mathbf{c}_2 \ldots \mathbf{c}_{M-2} \mathbf{c}_{M-1}$$

and then build a second row by selecting $\mathbf{e}_1$ (a vector not already written down) and adding it to the first row; thus,

$\mathbf{c}_0$	$\mathbf{c}_1$	$\mathbf{c}_2 \ldots \ldots \mathbf{c}_{M-2}$	$\mathbf{c}_{M-1}$
$\mathbf{e}_1$	$\mathbf{e}_1 + \mathbf{c}_1$	$\mathbf{e}_1 + \mathbf{c}_2 \ldots \mathbf{e}_1 + \mathbf{c}_{M-2}$	$\mathbf{e}_1 + \mathbf{c}_{M-1}$

A third row is created by picking $\mathbf{e}_2$ (a vector not already written down) and again adding it to the first row.

$\mathbf{c}_0$	$\mathbf{c}_1$	$\mathbf{c}_2 \ldots \ldots \mathbf{c}_{M-1}$
$\mathbf{e}_1$	$\mathbf{e}_1 + \mathbf{c}_1$	$\mathbf{e}_1 + \mathbf{c}_2 \ldots \mathbf{e}_1 + \mathbf{c}_{M-1}$
$\mathbf{e}_2$	$\mathbf{e}_2 + \mathbf{c}_1$	$\mathbf{e}_2 + \mathbf{c}_2 \ldots \mathbf{e}_2 + \mathbf{c}_{M-1}$

This procedure is repeated until no previously selected vectors remain. In the most recently written row, corresponding to $\mathbf{e}_i$, say, no vector $\mathbf{e}_i + \mathbf{c}_r = \mathbf{e}_j + \mathbf{c}_s$ where $j < i$, because this would imply that $\mathbf{e}_i = \mathbf{e}_j + (\mathbf{c}_s - \mathbf{c}_r) = \mathbf{e}_j + \mathbf{c}_k$ for some codeword $\mathbf{c}_k$, and this contradicts the rule that $\mathbf{e}_i$ has not been written down already.

Thus, the procedure terminates with a full row. Since there are 2^n vectors in total, M must divide 2^n; therefore, $M = 2^k$ for some k.

2.1.2 The Generator Matrix

The fact that $M = 2^k$ implies that the code is a k-dimensional subspace based on k linearly independent base vectors, g_i $i = 1$ to k say, and that the code consists of all linear combinations of these

$$c_j = \sum_{i=1}^{k} m_{ji} g_i \qquad m_{ji} = 0 \quad \text{or} \quad 1$$

We can then write this in matrix notation

$$c = mG \tag{2.2}$$

where m is a row-vector of k elements, and G is a (k by n) matrix, whose rows are the g_i.

Equation (2.2) is the formula used to generate a linear (n, k) code from k message elements (bits) using the generator matrix G.

The basis of the subspace can be changed without changing the space itself. Using standard matrix techniques, given that the g_i are linearly independent, we can add rows of G together (without changing the subspace) and reorder columns (which only means reordering the sequence in which we consider the bits in a vector) to produce

$$G = (I, P)$$

where I is the (k by k) identity matrix, and P is called the (k by $(n - k)$) *parity* matrix. This form of G results in a systematic (n, k) linear code giving

$$C = mG$$
$$= m(I, P)$$
$$= (m_1 m_2 \ldots m_k q_{k+1} q_{k+2} \ldots q_n)$$

with the first k bits being the unaltered message and the last $(n - k)$ bits, q_{k+1} to q_n, the check digits.

Using this representation we can summarise the code in Section 1.2, containing four codewords by its generator matrix

$$G = \begin{bmatrix} 10011111 \\ 01111100 \end{bmatrix}$$

The code of Section 1.1 with codewords (010) and (101) is not linear and cannot be represented in this way.

If we consider the subgroup within the code of all codewords **c** having a zero in a given position, for example, the first so that $\mathbf{c} = (0\ c_2 c_3 \dots c_n)$, we can then form a coset with a new vector $\mathbf{e}_1 = (100 \dots 0)$. This exhausts all the codewords, because if one remained, $\mathbf{c}_1$, say, it would necessarily have a 1 in the first position, and then $(\mathbf{c}_1 + \mathbf{e}_1)$ would be a codeword $\mathbf{c}_2$ in the original subgroup, so that $\mathbf{c}_1 = (\mathbf{c}_2 + \mathbf{e}_1)$, which contradicts the assumption that $\mathbf{c}_1$ has not been written down already. Therefore, the original subgroup comprises half the code, so that *over all codewords any bit position has an equal number of 0's and 1's*. This is illustrated in the code with codewords (00000000), (01111100), (10011111), and (11100011), previously considered.

2.2 THE NULL MATRIX OR PARITY-CHECK MATRIX

Constructing codewords from the generating matrix is a simple procedure, although it does suppose that one performs calculations with the $(k \cdot (n-k))$ parity matrix **P** to form the check digits. If k is large, for example, of the order 10^4 or 10^5, the storage and computing requirements may begin to become onerous. In the next chapter we shall see how the need to store **P** can be overcoming because further internal consistency, beyond mere linearity, is imposed on the code structure. A proper understanding of this can be obtained only by considering the *null matrix*, **H**, of a code. (In this book we use the term null matrix, which best expresses its principal property. The term *parity-check matrix* is also frequently used.)

The null matrix is formed from $(n-k)$ linearly independent vectors orthogonal to the code's basic vectors and hence orthogonal to all codevectors. By orthogonal we mean that the innerproduct

$$(\mathbf{c}_1 \cdot \mathbf{c}_2) = \sum_i c_{1i} c_{2i} = 0.$$

These $(n-k)$ vectors define the *nullspace*, and (as with the code itself) we have liberty in choosing a basis for the nullspace. If **G** is in systematic form, we can choose a particularly convenient form for the rows of the $((n-k) \cdot n)$ matrix **H** as follows:

$$\mathbf{G} = (\mathbf{I}, \mathbf{P}) \qquad (k \cdot n)$$
$$\mathbf{H} = (\mathbf{P}^T, \mathbf{I}) \qquad ((n-k) \cdot n)$$

(2.3)

where the superscript T indicates the transpose of the matrix in question, that is, rows and columns interchanged. It is easily verified that

$$\mathbf{GH}^T = \mathbf{0} \quad (k \cdot k) \tag{2.4}$$

proving that the rows of $\mathbf{H}$ indeed define the nullspace.

Note that some caution is required when considering $\mathbf{H}$. In ordinary matrices over an infinite field, if a vector is orthogonal to a subspace it is linearly independent of that subspace; if it is linearly independent of a subspace, it has a component orthogonal to that subspace. This means that a vectorspace can be split into a subspace and its null space, which between them contain all the vectors of the space. But over a finite field a vector *can be orthogonal to itself*. Over GF(2) every vector with an even number of bits is orthogonal to itself. That the nullspace of a code is of dimension $(n - k)$ can be seen by considering a vector with $2^{(n-k)}$ arbitrary codes in the last $(n - k)$ positions and noting that the first k positions are then determined uniquely by the orthogonality requirement when the vector is multiplied into the k rows of $\mathbf{G}$ in systematic form. The nullspace of $\mathbf{G}$, $\mathbf{H}$, and $\mathbf{G}$ itself do not necessarily span the space; so that there are vectors that are neither linearly dependent on the rows of $\mathbf{G}$ nor on the rows of $\mathbf{H}$. For example, if

$$\mathbf{G} = \begin{pmatrix} 1001 \\ 0101 \\ 0011 \end{pmatrix} \quad \text{then } \mathbf{H} = (1111)$$

and the nullspace is contained in the code. A vector such as (1000) is neither in the code nor in the nullspace.

From Equations (2.2) and (2.4) we get

$$\mathbf{s} = \mathbf{cH}^T = \mathbf{mGH}^T = \mathbf{0} \quad (1 \cdot (n - k)) \tag{2.5}$$

where $\mathbf{s}$ is an $(n - k)$ vector called the *syndrome* of $\mathbf{c}$. Equation (2.5) shows that we can test if a vector is a codeword by evaluating its syndrome and seeing if it is zero, because if the vector is in the null space of $\mathbf{H}$, then it must lie in the code.

2.2.1 The Syndrome

If we apply this test to a received vector

$$\mathbf{r} = \mathbf{c} + \mathbf{e}$$

where $\mathbf{c}$ is a codeword, $\mathbf{e}$ an error pattern, we get

$$\mathbf{s} = \mathbf{rH}^T = (\mathbf{c} + \mathbf{e})\mathbf{H}^T$$
$$\mathbf{s} = \mathbf{eH}^T \tag{2.6}$$

Equation (2.6) states that the syndrome of a received vector depends only on the error pattern and is independent of the codeword. Moreover, it is clear that if $\mathbf{s}_1$ and $\mathbf{s}_2$ are two distinct syndromes, then the corresponding errors $\mathbf{e}_1$ and $\mathbf{e}_2$ are distinct, except for the possible addition of a codeword. We can thus identify error patterns with weight $w \le t$, where the distance $d = 2t + 1$, by looking at the syndrome of the received vector, because such error patterns cannot differ by a codeword. There is a one-to-one correspondence between syndromes and error patterns with $w \le t$.

There are 2^{n-k} possible distinct syndromes, and $\binom{n}{w}$ distinct error patterns of weight w; therefore, for t-error correction we require

$$1 + \binom{n}{1} + \binom{n}{2} \ldots + \binom{n}{t} \le 2^{n-k} \tag{2.7}$$

This is (1.1) of Chapter 1 rewritten with $M = 2^k$ for a linear code.

Reverting to the standard array introduced previously, we now form it with the $\mathbf{e}_i$ chosen as the most likely error patterns: first, all the $\binom{n}{1}$ single-error patterns, then the $\binom{n}{2}$ two errors patterns, and so on. This procedure can continue up to all t-error patterns, if $d = 2t + 1$ is the distance of the code. As we go beyond t-error patterns, ambiguities arise, because we will find that some values $(\mathbf{c} + \mathbf{e})$ have been written down already. To illustrate this ambiguity, consider the $d = 4$ code with

$$\mathbf{G} = \begin{bmatrix} 10001011 \\ 01001110 \\ 00101101 \\ 00010111 \end{bmatrix} \qquad \mathbf{H} = \begin{bmatrix} 11101000 \\ 01110100 \\ 11010010 \\ 10110001 \end{bmatrix}$$

If we choose $\mathbf{e} = (00000011)$ of weight 2 for the first weight $- 2$ row of the standard array, we will (for example) write down (10001000) in that row, being $(\mathbf{g}_1 + \mathbf{e})$. Now we cannot choose $\mathbf{e}' = (10001000)$ for the next row. Alternatively if we had chosen $\mathbf{e}'$ for the first weight $- 2$ row, we could not choose $\mathbf{e}$ for the next one. Note that the syndrome of $\mathbf{e}$ and $\mathbf{e}'$ is (0011), that is, the same for both error patterns. However, as shown above, there is no such problem with single-error patterns, *all* of which give distinct syndromes, namely, the rows of $\mathbf{H}^T$ (the columns of $\mathbf{H}$).

This suggests a simple technique for correcting correctable error patterns, of weight less than or equal to t, in a received vector $\mathbf{r}$, namely:

1. Evaluate the syndrome, $\mathbf{s}$, from $\mathbf{r}$.
2. Look up the corresponding $\mathbf{e}$ in a precomputed table. (If the $\mathbf{s}$ found is not in the table the error is not correctable.)
3. The correct codeword $\mathbf{c} = \mathbf{r} + \mathbf{e}$.

(This technique is equivalent to finding $\mathbf{r}$ in a column in the standard array and picking the $\mathbf{c}$ at the head of that column as the correct codeword.)

2.2.2 The Columns of the Null Matrix

It was remarked that the columns of $\mathbf{H}$ are the syndromes corresponding to single errors. In fact the columns of $\mathbf{H}$ have a further significance: *The distance (weight) of a linear code is the minimum number of linearly dependent columns of H*. This follows from the fact that a codeword of that weight multiplied into $\mathbf{H}^T$ must give a zero syndrome; and no lower-weight codewords exist. This fact suggests a method for constructing codes in which the number of check-digits $(n-k)$ is chosen, the number of rows of $\mathbf{H}$, and suitable linearly independent columns are created to give a required distance, until we can add no more, and then we have n. This process is used in establishing the Varsharmov-Gilbert bound (see [2.4]), and in the construction of cyclic codes, as will be shown in the next chapter.

We finish this section by illustrating some of the points made with the $(5,2)$ code defined by

$$\mathbf{G} = \begin{bmatrix} 10110 \\ 01011 \end{bmatrix} \qquad \mathbf{H} = \begin{bmatrix} 10100 \\ 11010 \\ 01001 \end{bmatrix}$$

The columns of $\mathbf{H}$ are distinct; therefore, the distance $d \geq 3$. In fact $d = 3$, because the rows of $\mathbf{G}$ have weight 3, that is, columns 1, 3, 4 and 2, 4, 5 of $\mathbf{H}$ are linearly dependent. All single error patterns are correctable and we can write down the standard array with the syndromes (the rows of $\mathbf{H}^T$) added on the right.

$\mathbf{c}_0$	$\mathbf{c}_1$	$\mathbf{c}_2$	$\mathbf{c}_3$	$\mathbf{s}$
00000	10110	01011	11101	000
10000	**00110**	11011	01101	110
01000	11110	**00011**	10101	011
00100	**10010**	01111	11001	100
00010	**10100**	**01001**	11111	010
00001	10111	**01010**	11100	001
11000	01110	10011	**00101**	101
10001	00111	11010	**01100**	111

Above the broken line is a one-to-one correspondence between the coset leader, that is, the error pattern in column $\mathbf{c}_0$, and the syndrome. Below the broken line, where we consider 2-error patterns, there is ambiguity. Both 11000 and 00101 give the same syndrome, 101. We could have chosen 00101 as coset leader, without changing the content of the coset, merely its internal order. If the change were made we would decode 11000 to 11101 at the head of the column, rather than to 00000. (In the standard array the vectors of weight $= 2$ have been highlighted.)

2.3 PERFECT CODES

For a given $(n - k)$ and n, (2.7) gives an upper bound for the number of correctable bits in error, t. An (n, k) linear code for which the inequality becomes an equality is called a *perfect code*. The (23, 12) Golay code [5] is an example of a perfect code, with $t = 3$, $d = 7$, and $1 + 23 + 253 + 1771 = 2048 = 2^{11}$.

Simpler examples of perfect codes are the Hamming codes [3], with $t = 1$, $d = 3$ so that $1 + n = 2^{n-k}$.

For Hamming codes we have then

n	$(n - k)$	k
3	2	1
7	3	4
15	4	11
31	5	26
$\vdots$	$\vdots$	$\vdots$

Note that if $1 + n = 2^{n-k}$ then the number of columns of **H**, n, is given by $n = 2^{n-k} - 1$. That is, since **H** has $(n - k)$ rows, all $(2^{n-k} - 1)$ distinct nonzero bit patterns for the columns of **H** can be accommodated, giving a distance $d = 3$, because no fewer than three columns can be linearly dependent. This situation is illustrated in the (7, 4) Hamming code with

$$\mathbf{G} = \begin{pmatrix} 1000101 \\ 0100111 \\ 0010110 \\ 0001011 \end{pmatrix} \qquad \mathbf{H} = \begin{pmatrix} 1110100 \\ 0111010 \\ 1101001 \end{pmatrix}$$

Another example of perfect codes is given by the *repetition* codes, which have $n = 2t + 1$, $k = 1$. With $t = (n - 1)/2$

$$1 + \binom{n}{1} + \binom{n}{2} + \cdots + \binom{n}{t} = \frac{2^n}{2} = 2^{n-1} = 2^{n-k}$$

There is one information bit and $(n - 1)$ check digits. For example, with $n = 5$ the codevectors are (00000) and (11111),

$$G = (11111) \qquad H = \begin{pmatrix} 11000 \\ 10100 \\ 10010 \\ 10001 \end{pmatrix}$$

and $d = 5$, $t = 2$.

Linear codes whose weight is an odd number can have their distance increased by adding an extra bit to the code length, n, and setting that bit to 0 or 1 to give all base codewords (i.e., rows of **G**) even parity (i.e., an even number of 1's). This procedure cannot reduce the distance (since the original n bits are unaltered) but ensures that *all* codewords have even parity, since linear combinations of even-parity vectors give more-even-parity vectors. Therefore the minimum weight, which was odd, must have been increased by at least 1. As an example of this procedure consider the $(7, 4)$ Hamming code $(d = 3)$ extended to an $(8, 4)$ code with $d = 4$; thus,

$$G = \begin{pmatrix} 10001011 \\ 01001110 \\ 00101101 \\ 00010111 \end{pmatrix} \qquad H = \begin{pmatrix} 11101000 \\ 01110100 \\ 11010010 \\ 11111111 \end{pmatrix}$$

G has had parity bits added in an eighth position. **H** has had zeroes added in the eighth position so as to leave the existing orthogonality unchanged. **H** has also had an all-1's fourth row added to ensure the even parity of all codewords multiplied into it. **H** can be put in more normal form by subtracting the sum of the first three rows from the last, to give

$$H = \begin{pmatrix} 11101000 \\ 01110100 \\ 11010010 \\ 10110001 \end{pmatrix}$$

2.4 FURTHER BOUNDS ON LINEAR CODES

2.4.1 The Varsharmov-Gilbert Bound

The sphere-packing bound of Inequality (2.7) is attained by perfect codes, of which the repetition, Hamming, and Golay codes are the only known examples. Given the number of check digits $(n - k)$, it imposes an upper bound on the distance d, or more precisely on $t = (d - 1)/2$. On the other hand, given $(n - k)$ we can, as suggested in (2.2), always construct linear codes up to a certain limit by choosing columns of **H** to be suitably linearly independent. The limit is given by the Varsharmov-Gilbert bound [6] as follows:

Suppose we have constructed $(n - 1)$ columns of **H** subject to the constraint that all linear combinations of j columns, $j \le 2t$, are linearly independent. Then we pick a new column **x** that is not equal to any linear combination of $(2t - 1)$ of the existing columns. No $2t$ columns of the (now) n columns are linearly dependent; if they were, it would be a contradiction of the assumptions about the first $(n - 1)$ columns and the choice of the nth column. But for this choice to be possible, in the worst case when all j linear combinations produce distinct values, we must have

$$\binom{n-1}{1} + \binom{n-1}{2} + \cdots + \binom{n-1}{2t-1} < 2^{n-k} - 1 \qquad (2.8)$$

where $(2^{n-k} - 1)$ is the maximum number of nonzero columns.

For large n, (2.8) becomes

$$2^{(n-1)H(m)} < 2^{(n-k)}$$

with $m = (2t - 1)/(n - 1)$; see Appendix B. We may rephrase this as follows:

Provided that $nH(m) < (n - k)$, which implies (2.8), we can certainly construct a linear code of distance $(2t + 1)$. For large n this becomes

$$\text{coderate} = k/n < 1 - H(2t/n) \qquad (2.9)$$

If (2.9) is satisfied, we can certainly construct an (n, k) linear code capable of correcting t errors. This should be contrasted with the sphere-packing bound

$$k/n < 1 - H(t/n) \qquad (2.10)$$

Inequality (2.10) must be satisfied, since codes that do not satisfy it are impossible; but if (2.9) is satisfied, we can always find a linear code. The grey area where we must look for "good" codes with large k/n given t/n, or large t/n given k/n is

$$1 - H(2t/n) < k/n < 1 - H(t/n)$$

2.4.2 The Plotkin Bound

The sphere-packing bound, in its general form of inequality (1.2) in Chapter 1, applies to all codes. The Plotkin bound [7] is another upper bound on the code rate specific to linear codes. It is found as follows:

1. Let $M(n, t)$ be the maximum number of codewords, given n and t. Then consider the corresponding code of length n and its subgroup consisting of all codewords with 0 in the last position. This subgroup (dropping the last bit) is a code of length $(n-1)$, with $\leq M(n-1, t)$ codewords by hypothesis. But the subgroup is half the original code, so

$$M(n, t)/2 \leq M(n-1, t)$$

or

$$M(n, t) \leq 2M(n-1, t)$$

Note that this very simple expression states that for given t, as n increases by 1 bit, the number of codewords *at most* doubles. This is a severe restriction on the coderate k/n imposed *only* by linearity.

2. Now consider the total weight of all codewords:

$$\text{Total weight} = 2^k n/2$$
$$= 2^{k-1} n$$

(This is because half the bits in the code are 1, half 0, as shown in [2.1]). The average weight of the nonzero codewords is the total weight divided by $(2^k - 1)$, so the minimum weight or distance $d = 2t + 1$ satisfies

$$d(2^k - 1) \leq 2^{k-1} n$$

so

$$2^k \leq 2d/(2d - n)$$

provided that $(2d - n) > 0$.

3. For the optimum code with maximum codewords

$$M(n, t) = 2^k \leq 2d/(2d - n) \qquad (\text{if } (2d - n) > 0)$$

Given d, we consider the largest $n = n^*$ such that

$$2d - n^* > 0, \qquad \text{namely, } n^* = 2d - 1$$

Then $M(n^*, t) \leq 2d$

For larger n we apply the inequality of step 1 repeatedly to get

$$2^k = M(n, t) \leq 2^{n-n^*} M(n^*, t) \leq 2^{(n+1-2d)} \cdot 2d$$

therefore,

$$k \leq n + 2 - 2d + \log_2 d$$

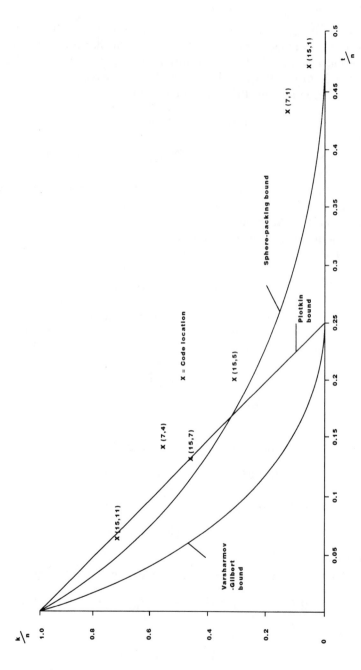

Figure 2.1 Bounds on coderate and t/n for large n.

4. We conclude that, if $n \geq n^* = 2d - 1$

$$(n - k) \geq 2d - 2 - \log_2 d$$

For large $n \geq 2d - 1 = 4t + 1$ we can write this:

$$\text{coderate} = k/n \leq 1 - 4t/n \qquad (2.11)$$

Inequality (2.11) is the Plotkin bound for linear codes. It is clear from Figure 2.1, that for high values of t/n this bound is more confining than the sphere-packing bound.

2.4.3 Bounds in Practice

It is worth looking at some real codes in the light of these various bounds.

Shannon's theorem states that it is possible to find a code that will correct np errors, where p is the bit error rate, with arbitrary small probability of error, provided that the coderate is less than the capacity.

Consider $p = 1/7$, so that the capacity $C = 1 - H(p) = 0.408$. The probability of decoding failure is the probability that more than t bit errors occur. The $(7,4)$ Hamming code corrects $np = 1$ bit error. But the coderate $k/n = 0.571$ (i.e., in excess of the capacity), and the probability of a decoding failure (i.e., more than a single error) is 0.264. We can reduce the coderate to 0.143, by using the $(7,1)$ repetition code, with $t = 3$ and the Prob(Failure) = 0.01. This is certainly much smaller than 0.264 but not negligible; and the coderate is well below the capacity. We are nowhere near the theoretical optimum given by Shannon, despite using "perfect" codes, and this is because n is small.

If we try the $(15,11)$ Hamming code as an example of a larger n, with $p = 1/15$ and $C = 0.646$, we can still correct $np = 1$ errors, but $k/n = 0.733$ (in excess of C) and the Prob(Failure) = 0.264. Reducing the coderate to 0.067 by using the $(15,1)$ repetition code gives a Prob(Failure) $< 5 \times 10^{-6}$. This is certainly approaching what one might call "arbitrary small" probability of error, but with a coderate an order of magnitude less than C.

Table 2.1 presents the $(15,7)$ $d = 5$, and $(15,5)$ $d = 7$ codes in addition to those already introduced. In the table are values for the coderate k/n, the ratio t/n, and the Prob(Failure) assuming the bit-error probability p is $1/7$ and $1/15$. It can be seen that only when $k/n \ll C$ does Prob(Failure) start to decrease and we have $t/n \gg p$ in these cases; whereas according to Shannon's theorem $t/n \sim p$ can give negligible Prob(Failure).

In Table 2.1 the Prob(Failure) values corresponding to $k/n < C$ have been highlighted. The codes have also been plotted on Figure 2.1. Shannon's theorem

Table 2.1

Code	t	k/n	t/n	Prob (Failure) $p = 1/7 = 0.143$	Prob (Failure) $p = 1/15 = 0.067$
(7, 4)	1	0.571	0.143	0.264	**0.075**
(7, 1)	3	0.143	0.429	**0.010**	6×10^{-4}
(15, 11)	1	0.733	0.067	0.653	0.264
(15, 7)	2	0.467	0.133	0.365	**0.074**
(15, 5)	3	0.333	0.200	**0.156**	0.015
(15, 1)	7	0.067	0.467	**0.005**	5×10^{-6}
				$C = 0.408$	$C = 0.646$

indicates that as n becomes much larger the situation should improve, but there is very little evidence of this from Table 2.1 (which, it must be admitted, has n small, although it has been doubled, from 7 to 15).

Ideally we want to maintain k/n, near the capacity, and hold t/n constant near the sphere-packing or Plotkin boundary, while progressively reducing Prob(Failure) as n increases. If we *can* manage to hold t/n constant, then we shall certainly reduce the probability of decoding failure, because

$$\text{Prob(Failure)} = 1 - \sum_{i=0}^{t} (1-p)^{n-i} p^i \binom{n}{i}$$

tends to zero $i = 0$ as n increases, for constant t/n. See Appendix B, expression (B.2).

It is also intuitively obvious that a single long codeword is better than a concatenation of short ones if we can maintain k/n and t/n as we lengthen n, because it can handle a burst of t or fewer errors anywhere in it. A concatenation of short codewords cannot do so, for the same value of t; the errors must be suitably distributed over the individual codewords. But the problem remains: How do we find the long codes that are promised by Shannon's theorem?

Finally we note that we have taken Prob(Failure) to be equal to the probability of $(t + 1)$ or more bit errors, when the code has distance $d = 2t + 1$. This is true for a perfect code, but for most codes there is the ambiguous range of error patterns giving rise to received vectors at a distance greater than t from any codeword. These errors are *detectable*, and so, while error correction may fail, it is not true to say that a false result will be produced. The decoding procedure can explicity flag such cases and recovery can be made by other means, for example, retransmission. Detectable error patterns are, as we have seen, patterns that are not codewords. Thus, an analysis of detectable errors requires an analysis of the probability of error patterns in the form of codewords, the undetectable errors-all the rest are detectable. In turn this requires an analysis of the *weight distribution* of the code, the number of codewords of weight i, w_i, for $i = 0$ to n. For example, for the $(7, 4)$ code we have

$$w_0 = 1, \quad w_1 = 0, \quad w_2 = 0, \quad w_3 = 7, \quad w_4 = 7, \quad w_5 = 0, \quad w_6 = 0, \quad w_7 = 1$$

A more thorough analysis of the probabilities of successful error correction, error detection without correction, and outright failure or incorrect "correction" must take into account the weight distribution of the code, as opposed to considering only the length and distance, as we have done.

2.5 NONBINARY LINEAR CODES

A nonbinary linear code is a subspace of a vector space over a finite field $GF(q)$, where $q = p^m$ and p is prime. Appendix C presents finite fields, and it is shown there that a finite field must have a prime *characteristic*, p, such that $(1 + 1 + \cdots + 1)$ p times sums to zero. It is also shown that the total number of elements in the field is $q = p^m$ for some integer m and that the $(q - 1)$ nonzero elements form a multiplicative group with a primitive element α, say, such that $\alpha^{q-1} = 1$.

A nonbinary (n, k) linear code thus consists of q^k codewords, each one being a vector of n *symbols* in length, where the symbols represent one of the q field elements. Addition and subtraction of vectors is pairwise by the field elements; scalar multiplication uses the multiplication rules of the field.

For example, in GF(3)

$$(1,2,0) + (2,2,1) = (0,1,1)$$
$$(1,2,0) - (2,2,1) = (2,0,2)$$
and
$$2(1,2,0) = (2,1,0)$$

In just the same way as we did for binary linear codes we can define a $(k \times n)$ generating matrix

$$\mathbf{G} = (\mathbf{I}, \mathbf{P})$$

It is important to note that the $(n - k)$ by n null matrix $\mathbf{H}$ contains $-\mathbf{P}^T$, because $1 + 1 \neq 0$ in general except when $p = 2$, so that

$$\mathbf{H} = (-\mathbf{P}^T, \mathbf{I})$$

We can form the standard array as in the binary case, but this time there are $(q - 1)^r \binom{n}{r}$ coset leaders of weight r; as opposed to simply $\binom{n}{r}$ when $q = 2$. To be able to correct t symbols in error we require

$$1 + (q - 1)\binom{n}{1} + (q - 1)^2\binom{n}{2} \ldots + (q - 1)^t\binom{n}{t} \leq q^{n-k}$$

as a new form of the sphere-packing bound.

Over GF(q) we can define Hamming codes using the columns of the null matrix. We require that the minimum weight of the code is 3, so all columns of **H** must be distinct, including the fact that no column must be a scalar multiple of any other. (This was irrelevant with $q = 2$, as the only nonzero scalar available for multiplication was 1.) This can be achieved if we consider the columns in sequence with the leading $(n - k - 1)$, $(n - k - 2)$, and so on, positions equal to zero and the first nonzero position made equal to 1. For example, over GF(3) with $(n - k) = 3$ we have

$$\mathbf{H} = \begin{pmatrix} 0000111111111 \\ 0111000111222 \\ 1012012012012 \end{pmatrix}$$

So $n = 13$, and we have an $(13, 10)$ code over GF(3) with $d = 3$ symbols. In systematic form we might write

$$\mathbf{H} = \begin{pmatrix} 0011111111100 \\ 1100111222010 \\ 1212012012001 \end{pmatrix}$$

In general there exist

$$1 + q + q^2 + q^3 \ldots + q^{n-k-1}$$

such columns; therefore

$$n = (q^{n-k} - 1)/(q - 1)$$

for a nonbinary Hamming code.

If we consider error correction with such a code, we follow the previous procedure of evaluating

$$\mathbf{r}\mathbf{H}^T = \mathbf{e}\mathbf{H}^T = \mathbf{s}$$

where **r** is the received vector, **e** the error vector, and **s** the syndrome. The scalar product of a column of **H** will be **s** if only a single symbol error occurs, and this will enable us to *locate* the error postion. To calculate the error *value* (because it is not necessarily equal to 1 as is the case for binary codes) we use the parity checks. For example, suppose **c** is sent using the $(13, 10)$ code illustrated,

$$\mathbf{c} = (0100000000021)$$

that is, the second row of **G**, remembering to change the sign as well as transpose the parity matrix in **H**. And suppose the error is

$$\mathbf{e} = (0020000000000)$$

Then
$$\mathbf{r} = (0120000000021)$$

and
$$\mathbf{s} = (0 + 2 + 0 + 0, 1 + 0 + 2 + 0, 2 + 2 + 0 + 1)$$
$$= (202)$$
$$= 2(101)$$

therefore, the error is located in the third symbol position, because this is the position where $\mathbf{H}^T$ has a row (101). We can conclude directly that the error value is 2, but it may be more illuminating to do the following: Let x be the correct value for the position, so **c** is **r** with x in the third position.

$$\mathbf{c} = (01x0000000021)$$

Then, since $\mathbf{cH}^T = \mathbf{0}$ we find $x = 0$

The above procedure is typical of nonbinary error correction. Two steps are used:

1. Locate the position of the symbols in error.
2. Evaluate the values corresponding to those positions.

(There are up to $(n - k)$ equations in principle available for this, from the requirement $\mathbf{cH}^T = \mathbf{0}$.)

The reasoning that was used (based on cosets of the subspace consisting of all codewords with a zero in a given position) in (2.1) can be extended to show that

In a code over GF(q) each symbol position has an equal number of all symbol values, namely $q^k/q = q^{k-1}$. We can use this in step 2 of calculating the Plotkin bound in (2.4) to give for large n

$$\text{coderate} = k/n \leq 1 - 2q\,t/n$$

which is the new Plotkin bound for codes over GF(q).

2.5.1 Nonbinary Codes with Characteristic 2

In practice, when digital computers are used, it is most convenient to choose GF(q) to have characteristic $p = 2$, so $q = 2^m$.

In accordance with Appendix C we represent the field by the residues of an irreducible polynomial of degree m over GF(2). It is normal to take the polynomial as primitive, because that allows us to represent all nonzero field elements in one of two ways, as convenient.

Thus, if α is the primitive root of the chosen polynomial we can consider elements as patterns of m bits, each postion corresponding to a power of α, α^i $i = 0, (m - 1)$;

$$\alpha^{m-1}, \alpha^{m-2}, \ldots, \alpha^3, \alpha^2, \alpha^1, \alpha^0$$

so that, for example if $m = 4$, 1011 means

$$\alpha^3 + \alpha + 1$$

This form is suitable for *adding* field elements, because $p = 2$, so addition is the familiar exclusive OR.

Alternatively, we can represent elements by their power of α, so that multiplication and division become simple. This is done by adding or subtracting exponents modulo $(2^m - 1)$, since $\alpha^{2^m - 1} = 1$

As an example consider GF(2^3) defined by $x^3 + x + 1$. The nonzero elements are tabulated in Table 2.2; the first column being the exponent of α, the second the representation of the element as a 3-bit vector.

From Table 2.2 we can see that $\alpha^5 + \alpha^6 = (111) + (101) = (010) = \alpha$, while $\alpha^5 \cdot \alpha^6 = \alpha^{11} = \alpha^4$. We may use the two representations of the field elements in the

Table 2.2

i	α^2	α	1
0	0	0	1
1	0	1	0
2	1	0	0
3	0	1	1
4	1	1	0
5	1	1	1
6	1	0	1
7	0	0	1

manner we find most convenient. As an example, consider the $(7,3)$ code over $GF(2^3)$ defined by

$$\mathbf{G} = \begin{pmatrix} 100\alpha & \alpha^3\alpha^6\alpha^6 \\ 0101 & \alpha^4\alpha^2\alpha \\ 001\alpha^2\alpha^5 & \alpha^5\alpha^6 \end{pmatrix}$$

$$= \begin{pmatrix} 001000000010011101101 \\ 000001000001110100010 \\ 000000001100111111101 \end{pmatrix}$$

with
$$\mathbf{H} = \begin{pmatrix} \alpha & 1 & \alpha^2 1000 \\ \alpha^3\alpha^4\alpha^5 0100 \\ \alpha^6\alpha^2\alpha^5 0010 \\ \alpha^6\alpha & \alpha^6 0001 \end{pmatrix}$$

Suppose we receive $\mathbf{r} = (\alpha^2\alpha 1\alpha^4 0\alpha^5 1)$, a 7-symbol, 21-bit stream, and suppose we are told the code can correct two symbol errors, and two errors are known to exist in positions 1 and 6 of $\mathbf{r}$. Then we can evaluate

$$\mathbf{r} = (x\alpha 1\alpha^4 0y1)$$

by multiplication into the columns of $\mathbf{H}$ to find a syndrome $(\alpha x, \alpha^3 x, \alpha^6 x + \alpha^2 + y, \alpha^6 x)$. Since this must be zero, we deduce $x = 0$, $y = \alpha^2$, so the corrected received vector is $(0\alpha 1\alpha^4 0\alpha^2 1)$. This is, in fact,

$$\alpha(\text{2nd row of } \mathbf{G}) + (\text{3rd row of } \mathbf{G})$$

Note that in this example of calculations over $GF(2^m)$ we did not explain the origins of the code or its property of correcting two symbol errors. It is, in fact, a Reed-Solomon code.

Chapter 3
Cyclic Codes

3.1 THE GENERATING POLYNOMIAL

In Chapter (2), a linear code was defined as a subspace of a linear vector space. We now introduce *multiplication* into the vector space by considering the elements in each vector as coefficients of a polynomial. Thus,

$$a(x) = a_{n-1}x^{n-1} + a_{n-2}x^{n-2} + \cdots + a_1 x + a_0$$

is our new representation of the *n*-vector

$$(a_{n-1}a_{n-2} \cdots a_1 a_0)$$

with the elements a_i taken from the finite field, which for the moment we assume to be GF(2).

The multiplication of vectors $\mathbf{a}, \mathbf{b}$ is now given by

$$\mathbf{c} \sim c(x) = a(x)b(x) \bmod (x^n - 1) \sim \mathbf{a} \cdot \mathbf{b}$$

That is, $c(x)$ is the remainder on dividing the product $a(x)b(x)$ by $(x^n - 1)$.

The *n*-dimensional vector space is now also a *ring* of 2^n polynomials, that is, a set of polynomials forming a group under addition and closed under multiplication. (Note that if the underlying field is GF(2) the modulus $(x^n - 1) = (x^n + 1)$.) A cyclic code is defined as an *ideal* in this ring. An ideal is an additive subgroup of the ring with the additional property that if $c(x)$ is a polynomial in the ideal, and $a(x)$ is any other polynomial (in the ideal or not), then $a(x)c(x)$ is in the ideal.

An immediate consequence of this definition is that if $c(x)$ is a codeword and we take $a(x) = x$, we get

$$d(x) = x.c(x) \bmod (x^n - 1)$$

$$= c_{n-1}x^n + c_{n-2}x^{n-1} + \cdots + c_1 x^2 + c_0 x \bmod (x^n - 1)$$

$$= c_{n-2}x^{n-1} + \cdots + c_1 x^2 + c_0 x + c_{n-1}$$

Thus, $d(x)$ is another codeword by the definition of the ideal, so that

A cyclic code is a subspace of a vector space with the additional property that all cyclic rotations of the elements of a codeword give rise to another codeword.

Thus, $(c_{n-1}c_{n-2} \ldots c_1 c_0)$ is a codeword implies that $(c_{n-2}c_{n-3} \ldots c_1 c_0 c_{n-1})$ is a codeword.

Within the code, there must exist a codeword polynomial of lower degree than any other, $g(x)$, say. $g(x)$ must also be unique, because if there were two $g_1(x), g_2(x)$ of the same minimal degree, we could construct a new polynomial of lower degree by subtraction—a contradiction.

Then, every codeword $c(x)$ is divisible by $g(x)$, because if it were not so, there would exist a remainder $r(x)$ of degree less than $g(x)$:

$$c(x) = g(x)q(x) + r(x)$$

where $q(x)$ is the quotient polynomial. But $g(x)q(x)$ is a codeword by definition of the ideal, and $c(x)$ is a codeword by assumption; therefore, $r(x)$ is a codeword of degree less than $g(x)$ – a contradiction. Therefore, $r(x) = 0$ identically, and $c(x) = g(x)q(x)$. $g(x)$ is called the *generating polynomial*.

$g(x)$ not only divides all "normal" codewords, it also divides $(x^n - 1)$, which is the null codeword.

To see this, consider $p(x)$, a codeword of degree $(n - 1)$. Then

$$r(x) = p(x)q(x) \bmod (x^n - 1)$$

is a codeword by definition, where $q(x)$ is any polynomial of degree greater than zero. Thus,

$$p(x)q(x) = r(x) + (x^n - 1)$$

But $g(x)$, the generating polynomial divides $p(x)$ and $r(x)$ because they are codewords; therefore, $g(x)$ divides $(x^n - 1)$ and

$$(x^n - 1) = g(x)h(x)$$

where $h(x)$ is the quotient.

If the degree of $g(x)$ is $(n - k)$, the cyclic code is an (n, k) linear code. Codewords can be generated from messages of k bits by regarding the message as a polynomial $m(x)$ of degree $(k - 1)$, that is, with 2^k possible values, and forming

$$c(x) = m(x)g(x)$$

to give $c(x)$, a codeword divisible by $g(x)$, of degree $(n - 1)$.

3.1.1 Systematic Cyclic Codes

As with all linear codes, cyclic codes can be put more conveniently in systematic form by considering $r_i(x)$, the remainder of degree $(n - k - 1)$ or less on dividing x^i by $g(x)$, for $i = 0$ to $(n - 1)$. The generating matrix $\mathbf{G}$ then has Row (j),

$$\text{Row } (j) = x^{n-j} - r_{n-j}(x) \qquad 1 \le j \le k \tag{3.1}$$

The null matrix $\mathbf{H}$ then has as Column (j)

$$\text{Column } (j) = \mathbf{r}_{n-j}^{\mathrm{T}}(x) \qquad 1 \le j \le n \tag{3.2}$$

Notice that this expression (3.2) for the columns of $\mathbf{H}$ holds even when $j > k$, in which case

$$\mathbf{r}_{n-j}(x) = x^{n-j}$$

(In (3.1) and (3.2) we of course consider only the *coefficients* of the polynomials in $\mathbf{G}$ and $\mathbf{H}$; the powers of x have to be imagined.)

The rows of $\mathbf{G}$ are divisible by $g(x)$, as they must be, as can be seen from (3.1). A codeword $\mathbf{c}$ multiplied into $\mathbf{H}^{\mathrm{T}}$ must give a zero syndrome, and it is easily verified that this occurs by cancellation of the check digits in the codeword with the appropriate sum of columns of $\mathbf{H}$. However, the most important conclusion from this systematic representation is that the syndrome of a general received vector $a(x)$ is simply the remainder on dividing it by $g(x)$, found by adding the remainders corresponding to the error-bits in $a(x) = c(x) + e(x)$, that is, the nonzero bits in $e(x)$.

To make this clear, consider $g(x) = x^4 + x + 1$, with $n = 15$. Ignoring minus signs since we are in GF(2), we find:

$$r_0(x) = 1 \quad r_1(x) = x, \quad r_2(x) = x^2, \quad r_3(x) = x^3$$

$$r_4(x) = x + 1 \quad r_5(x) = x^2 + x \quad r_6(x) = x^3 + x^2 \quad r_7(x) = x^3 + x + 1$$

$$r_8(x) = x^2 + 1 \quad r_9(x) = x^3 + x \quad r_{10}(x) = x^2 + x + 1 \quad r_{11}(x) = x^3 + x^2 + x$$

$$r_{12}(x) = x^3 + x^2 + x + 1 \quad r_{13}(x) = x^3 + x^2 + 1 \quad r_{14}(x) = x^3 + 1$$

Thus,

$$\mathbf{G} = \begin{bmatrix} 100000000001001 \\ 010000000001101 \\ 001000000001111 \\ 000100000001110 \\ 000010000000111 \\ 000001000001010 \\ 000000100000101 \\ 000000010001011 \\ 000000001001100 \\ 000000000100110 \\ 000000000010011 \end{bmatrix}$$

$$\mathbf{H} = \begin{bmatrix} 111101011001000 \\ 011110101100100 \\ 001111010110010 \\ 111010110010001 \end{bmatrix}$$

If $a(x) = x^8 + x^6 + x^3 + x^2$, division by $g(x) = x^4 + x + 1$ yields remainder $(x^2 + 1)$, which corresponds to $r_8(x)$, or column (7) of $\mathbf{H}$. This identifies the x_8 term of $a(x)$ as erroneous, because this is a (cyclic) Hamming code, as can be seen from $\mathbf{H}$, which contains all distinct nonzero 4-bit patterns for its columns.

For cyclic codes in systematic form we thus have a simple procedure for forming codewords and finding syndromes, as follows:

- To form a codeword from a message, $m(x)$, of degree less than or equal to $(k - 1)$ we write down $c(x) = x^{n-k}m(x) - r(x)$, where $r(x)$ is the remainder on dividing $x^{n-k}m(x)$ by $g(x)$.
- To evaluate a syndrome, $s(x)$, divide the received vector, $a(x)$, by $g(x)$ and evaluate the remainder, $s(x) = a(x) - g(x)q(x)$, where $q(x)$ is the quotient.

The importance of this is that, for cyclic codes, it is not necessary to hold matrices **G, H**, nor to perform calculations with them. (When the codes are binary, we may replace all minus signs with plus signs in the above description.) Note that in **G** (and **H**) all rows are formed from cyclic rotations and additions of one basic row.

3.2 THE ROOTS OF $g(x)$ AND THE NULL MATRIX

Since $g(x)$ divides all codewords and also $(x^n - 1)$, the roots of $g(x)$ are roots of all codewords and of $(x^n - 1)$. If α is a root of $g(x)$, since $\alpha^n = 1$ the order of x divides n.

In general $g(x)$ factorizes into one or more irreducible polynomials (irreducible over our basic field, e.g., GF(2)), so the roots of $g(x)$ lie in some extension field. For example, if $g(x)$ is itself irreducible of degree m, the roots of $g(x)$ (see Appendix C) are $\alpha^2, \alpha^4 \ldots \alpha^{2^{m-1}}$ and lie in the field GF(2^m). Each root satisfies $x^n = 1$, with $n = 2^m - 1$. If $g(x)$ is primitive, no smaller value of n is possible, since the order of α is $(2^m - 1)$. If $g(x)$ is irreducible but not primitive, n divides $(2^m - 1)$. If $g(x)$ is the product of two or more irreducible polynomials, the value of n is the lowest common multiple of the order of the roots of those irreducible factors of $g(x)$.

In (3.1) we had an example of $g(x)$ primitive with $m = 4, n = 2^m - 1 = 15$. As an example of a nonprimitive irreducible $g(x)$ consider $g(x) = x^4 + x^3 + x^2 + x + 1$.

If α is a root, we have $\alpha^5 + \alpha^4 + \alpha^3 + \alpha^2 + \alpha = 0$; therefore $\alpha^5 = 1$. Thus, α has order 5, and $g(x)$ divides $(x^5 - 1) = (x^5 + 1)$. In fact $(x^5 + 1) = g(x)(x + 1)$. In this case $n = 5, n - k = 4, k = 1$ and we have a (cyclic) (5, 1) repetition code. (Repetition codes are obviously cyclic.)

For an example of $g(x)$ not being irreducible, consider $g(x) = (x^3 + x + 1)$ $(x + 1) = x^4 + x^3 + x^2 + 1$. The order of the roots of $(x^3 + x + 1)$, which is primitive, is 7. The order of the root of $(x + 1)$ is 1. The least common multiple is 7. Therefore, $n = 7$ and we can form

$$\mathbf{G} = \begin{bmatrix} 1001110 \\ 0100111 \\ 0011101 \end{bmatrix} \qquad \mathbf{H} = \begin{bmatrix} 1011000 \\ 1110100 \\ 1100010 \\ 0110001 \end{bmatrix}$$

Adding all the rows of **H** together gives the row (1111111), which shows that this (7, 3) code has even parity, as is obvious from looking at the rows of **G**. It is also obvious that since $(x + 1)$ is a factor of all codewords, substituting $x = 1$ in those codewords results in adding together the nonzero coefficients to produce a zero result, that is, even parity. This technique is general, in the sense that we can convert any (n, k) code with $n = 2^m - 1$ and $n - k = m$ based on a primitive $g(x)$, which is necessarily of odd parity, into an even parity $(n, k - 1)$ code with a new generating polynomial $g(x)(1 + x)$.

However, the most important point to make about the roots of $g(x)$ is that, since they satisfy $c(x) = 0$, the vector $(\alpha^{n-1}\alpha^{n-2}\ldots\alpha^2\alpha1)$ must lie in the null space, where α is a root of $g(x)$, because

$$c(\alpha) = c_{n-1}\alpha^{n-1} + c_{n-2}\alpha^{n-2}\ldots c_2\alpha^2 + c_1\alpha + c_0 = 0 \qquad (3.3)$$

Accordingly an alternative representation for $\mathbf{H}$ is

$$\mathbf{H} = \begin{bmatrix} \alpha_1^{n-1}\alpha_1^{n-2}\ldots\alpha_1^2\alpha_1^1 \\ \text{-----------------} \\ \alpha_m^{n-1}\alpha_m^{n-2}\ldots\alpha_m^2\alpha_m1 \end{bmatrix} \qquad (3.4)$$

where the α_i for $i = 1$ to m are the roots of $g(x)$.

Equation (3.4) requires some explanation. If $g(x)$ is of degree $m = n - k$, there are, as there should be, $(n - k)$ rows in $\mathbf{H}$. However, if $g(x)$ is irreducible, only one row is necessary. This is because, over GF(2), the subsequent roots are $\alpha_i = \alpha_1^{2^{i-1}}$. (See Appendix C.) If α_1 satisfies (3.3), all α_i automatically satisfy it, as we can see by repeatedly squaring (3.3) and remembering that $1^2 = 1$ and that all cross terms have coefficient $2 = 0$. The same reasoning applies over GF(q) with

$$\alpha_i = \alpha_1^{q^{i-1}}$$

On the other hand, the $(n - k)$ rows of $\mathbf{H}$ are maintained in (3.4) even if we drop all α_i, $2 \le i \le m$, because the powers of α themselves form a vector of m elements, namely (dropping the subscript 1), linear combinations of $(00\ldots01)^\mathrm{T}, (00\ldots\alpha0)^\mathrm{T}, (00\ldots\alpha^200)^\mathrm{T}\ldots(\alpha^{m-1}0\ldots00)^\mathrm{T}$.

If $g(x)$ is the product of j irreducible polynomials, then $\mathbf{H}$ has j rows each of "dimension" m_i, where m_i is the degree of the jth factor and

$$\sum_{i=1,j} m_i = m = n - k$$

For an example, consider $g(x) = x^4 + x + 1$ with a root α. If we regard $\mathbf{H}$ as

$$\mathbf{H} = \begin{bmatrix} & & \alpha^3 \\ & & \alpha^2 \\ & & \alpha^1 \\ & & \alpha^0 \end{bmatrix}$$

where α^0 to α^3 represent the four rows of **H**, we see that we end up with precisely the same **H** as in the example of (3.1).

Yet another way of looking at the null matrix **H** is based on the fact that $g(x)$ divides $(x^n - 1)$, so

$$h(x) = (x^n - 1)/g(x)$$

$h(x)$ can be regarded as the generating polynomial of another, dual, cyclic code with codewords $d(x)$. Since $g(x)$ divides $c(x)$ (the original codevectors) and $h(x)$ divides $d(x)$, we have $g(x)h(x)$ divides $c(x)d(x)$; therefore, $c(x)d(x) = 0 \bmod(x^n - 1)$. If we consider any power of x, say, x^i, it has as coefficients the sum

$$\sum_{j=0, n-1} c_{i-j}d_j$$

with the subscript $(i - j)$ of c taken modulo $(n - 1)$. All such sums for $i = 0$ to $(n - 1)$ can be produced by multiplying k rotations of $c(x)$ into $(n - k)$ rotations of $d(x)$, using the inner product, and writing $d(x)$ in reverse order

$$(c_{n-1-i}c_{n-2-i} \cdots c_1 c_0 \cdots c_{n-i}) \cdot (d_{n-j}d_{n-j+1} \cdots d_{n-1}d_0 d_1 \cdots d_{n-j-1})$$

In terms of the **G** and **H** matrices and their bases, we can form **H** by writing the rows of **H** as $h(x)$ and cyclic shifts of it in reverse order. Thus, the left column of **H** corresponds to x^0, the next column to x^1, and so forth.

Thus, if $g(x) = x^4 + x + 1, h(x) = 1 + x + x^2 + x^3 + x^5 + x^7 + x^8 + x^{11} =$ (111101011001000).

This is the first row of **H** in the example of (3.1). The subsequent rows are formed by rotating this row and adding in previously created rows, as appropriate, to form the $(n - k)$ by $(n - k)$ identity matrix **I** at the right end.

Finally, we remark that the length of a cyclic code, n, is normally given by the least value of n, n^* say, such that $g(x)$ divides $(x^n - 1)$. We could of course choose $n = in^*$, where i is an integer (see Appendix C), but this would gain us nothing but merely reduce the distance to $d = 2$, since $x^n + 1$ is now a codeword. We cannot choose n less than n^*. We can, however, turn any cyclic code into a shortened cyclic code if we restrict $m(x)$, the message polynomial, to be of degree less than k by making the first few bits $(m_{k-1}, m_{k-2}$, etc.) always zero. This shortened code is a valid linear code in that it is a subspace. It is clearly not cyclic, however. The effect of making the first j coefficients of $m(x)$ zero is to shorten the length to $(n - j)$ and to make the first j rows of **G** and the first j columns of **H** unnecessary. A shortened cyclic code cannot have a lesser distance than the cyclic code from which it is derived.

3.3 ERROR DETECTION WITH CYCLIC CODES

The ability of a linear code to detect and correct errors depends on its distance properties, as discussed in Chapter 2. Since cyclic codes are linear, that discussion is still relevant. In the Chapter 4 we shall consider methods for constructing special classes of codes with predetermined distances. However, for the moment let us merely consider the distance properties and the error-detection capabilities of the types of cyclic codes we have already discussed.

First we remark that if the generating polynomial, $g(x)$, is primitive of degree m we necessarily have a Hamming code, with the null matrix having as columns all the powers α^i $i = 0$ to $(2^m - 2)$, as we have seen. Thus, a primitive $g(x)$ gives rise to $d = 3$.

If $g(x)$ is irreducible but nonprimitive, we have a code with a length n that divides $(2^m - 1)$ and a distance not less than 3, since the columns of $\mathbf{H}$ are still all distinct. With luck the distance is considerably greater. A good example of such a nonprimitive cyclic code is the Golay code, with $d = 7$ and $g(x) = x^{11} + x^9 + x^7 + x^6 + x^5 + x + 1$. In that case $n = 23$ (which divides $2^{11} - 1 = 2047$).

However, if we are really to create linearly independent columns of $\mathbf{H}$ that give a large distance; and if we recall how those columns are made up of powers of a root of each irreducible factor of $g(x)$ (see [3.1]), it is clear that we need to make $g(x)$ composite. Methods for constructing such composite $g(x)$ are considered in Chapter 4. But cyclic codes, even of limited distance, do have the ability to detect bursts of errors. Since any error pattern that gives rise to a nonzero syndrome, that is, a nonzero remainder on division by $g(x)$, is detectable, any single error burst of $(n - k)$ or fewer bits is detectable. In this case

$$e(x) = x^i\left(e_{n-k-1}x^{n-k-1} + e_{n-k-2}x^{n-k-2}\ldots + e_1x + e_0\right)$$

and this cannot be divisible by $g(x)$ of degree $(n - k)$; therefore, the syndrome remainder is nonzero.

Moreover, if $g(x)$ has $(x + 1)$ as a factor and $(x + 1)$ always divides $(x^n + 1)$ then all codewords $c(x)$ have $(x + 1)$ as a factor, that is, have even parity. Therefore, all error patterns that contain an odd number of error bits are detectable.

These observations point toward the use of a simple and common form for $g(x)$, namely, $g(x) = (1 + x)p(x)$, where $p(x)$ is a primitive polynomial, typically of degree 15, 23, or 31, so that $g(x)$ is of degree $(n - k) = 16$, 24, or 32.

Such a $g(x)$ gives rise to

- A code with $d \geq 4$ so that any three or fewer random bit errors are detectable.
- All odd numbers of bits in error are detectable.
- Any single error burst of $(n - k)$ or fewer bits in length is detectable.

The best known example of such a code is probably that of CCITT's Recommendation X.41, [8] based on the generating polynomial $g(x) = x^{16} + x^{12} + x^5 + 1 = (x+1)(x^{15} + x^{14} + x^{13} + x^{12} + x^4 + x^3 + x^2 + x + 1)$.

3.3.1 Weight Distributions

As pointed out in Chapter 2, a full analysis of the error-detection capabilities of a code requires knowledge of the weight distribution. If the code is cyclic, and the generating polynomial $g(x)$ does *not* have $(x+1)$ as a factor, then the polynomial

$$c(x) = x^{n-1} + x^{n-2} + x^{n-3} + \cdots + x^2 + x + 1$$

is a codeword. This is because

$$(x^n + 1) = (x+1)c(x)$$

and since $g(x)$ divides $(x^n + 1)$, it must divide $c(x)$. Such codes have a symmetrical weight distribution, in that the number of vectors of weight w is the same as the number of vectors of weight $(n-w)$; because then the complement $(a(x) + c(x))$ of any codeword $a(x)$ becomes another codeword. This facilitates the analysis of error detection. For example, the (15, 7) code with

$$g(x) = (x^4 + x + 1)(x^4 + x^3 + x^2 + x + 1) = x^8 + x^7 + x^6 + x^4 + 1$$

has the weight distribution shown in Table 3.1.

Table 3.1

Weight	Number of Codewords	Number of Possibilities
0	1	1
1	0	15
2	0	105
3	0	455
4	0	1365
5	18	3003
6	30	5005
7	15	6435
8	15	6435
9	30	5005
10	18	3003
11	0	1365
12	0	455
13	0	105
14	0	15
15	1	1
	$128 = 2^7$	$32768 = 2^{15}$

The first column gives the weight; the second, the number of codewords of that weight; the third, the number of possible n-vectors of that weight. Since all errors that are *not* codewords are detectable, we may make statements like these:

"All 1365 4-bit error patterns are detectable"

and

"6420 of all 7-bit error patterns are detectable, and that is 99.77% of all 7-bit error patterns"

3.3.2 Shortened Cyclic Codes and Feedback Shift Registers

Probably the most widely used method of error detection in digital computing is based on shortened cyclic codes. This means that the message is not constrained to be k bits in length, but rather j bits with $j \le k$. The number of check digits $(n - k)$ is, however, fixed. In most cases the value of j is not known in advance, so the technique used is to compute a sort of "running remainder" for the check digits, adjusting it each time a new message bit is presented. To explain this procedure, we alter the notation and call the message $(m_1 m_2 \ldots m_j)$, with m_1 the first bit. The complete codeword now becomes, after i message bits have been processed,

$$x^{n-k}m(x) + r(x)$$
$$= x^{n-k}\left(m_1 x^{i-1} + m_2 x^{i-2} + \cdots + m_{i-1}x + m_i\right)$$
$$+ r_{n-k-1}x^{n-k-1} + \cdots + r_1 x + r_0$$
$$= q(x)g(x)$$

where $r(x)$ is the remainder on dividing $x^{n-k}m(x)$ by $g(x)$, and $q(x)$ is the quotient.

With this notation, the appearance of a new message bit, m_{i+1}, gives rise to a new message, $m'(x)$:

$$m'(x) = x\,m(x) + m_{i+1}$$

The new value of $r'(x)$ can be calculated as follows. Since

$$x^{n-k}m(x) = r(x) \bmod g(x)$$
$$x^{n-k}\left(x\,m(x) + m_{i+1}\right) = x\,r(x) + m_{i+1}x^{n-k} \bmod g(x)$$

But the expression on the left is $x^{n-k}m'(x)$, and this modulo $g(x)$, is by definition $r'(x)$. Therefore,

$$r'(x) = xr(x) + m_{i+1}x^{n-k} \bmod g(x)$$

$$= x^{n-k}(m_{i+1} + r_{n-k-1}) \bmod g(x) + \left(r_{n-k-2}x^{n-k-1} + - + r_0 x\right)$$

because $g(x)$ is of degree $(n - k)$. Thus, to calculate the new remainder from the old:

1. Shift the old $r(x)$ left 1 bit (multiply by x).
2. Add (XOR) the new message bit m_{i+1} to the overflow remainder bit r_{n-k-1} from step 1.
3. If the result of step 2 is zero, the result of step 1 is $r'(x)$; otherwise, add (XOR) into the result of step 1 the terms of $g(x)$ with the exception of x^{n-k} to give $r'(x)$.

This process is easily performed by a feedback shift register circuit, as illustrated in Figure 3.1. In the figure the polynomial $x^{16} + x^{12} + x^5 + 1$ is used to make the example precise. One has to imagine message and remainder bits (in the register) being shifted in synchronism to the left, one at a time, and the result of step 2 being added back into the register. We can also perform the process simply in software, typically 8 bits at a time. That is, we process an octet, 8 new input bits $(m_{i+1}$ to $m_{i+8})$, each step as follows:

1. Shift the old $r(x)$ left one octet.
2. Add (XOR) the new message octet to the overflow octet from step 1 to produce $J(J = 0$ to $255)$
3. Use J as the index into a table T of 256 entries $T(J)$, each of $(n - k)$ bits, which represent the contribution to the new remainder of feeding back J eight times using the mod $g(x)$ process; and add (XOR) $T(J)$ into the result of step 1 to give the new remainder.

At each stage $r(x)$, the content of the register, is the remainder, that is, the check

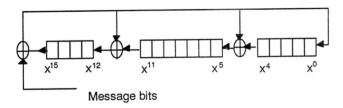

Message bits

Figure 3.1 Feedback shift register for dividing by $(x^{16} + x^{12} + x^5 + 1)$.

digits, associated with $m(x)$. If we stop when $i = j$, the initial $(k - j)$ bits of $m(x)$ are zero, so the code is a systematic cyclic code shortened by forcing the first $(k - j)$ bits to be zero. The circuit of Figure 3.1 effectively performs division.

This procedure can be used to generate codewords. It can also be used to detect errors. We can divide the entire received vector $(x^{n-k}m(x) + r(x))$ by $g(x)$ and check that the resultant remainder is zero. If the circuit of Figure 3.1 is used, we would then be processing $(j + n - k)$ bits, that is, dividing x^{n-k} times the received vector rather than the vector itself, but the criterion of a zero remainder for no detected errors still holds. Alternatively we can stop the process after dividing $x^{n-k}m''(x)$ by $g(x)$, where $m''(x)$ is $m(x)$ after possible corruption by errors, and compare the $r(x)$ calculated from this with the received $r''(x)$. If they are not equal, an error has been detected.

3.4 ERROR CORRECTION WITH CYCLIC CODES

Correcting errors in received cyclic codewords is, as usual, much more complex than merely detecting them. If $g(x)$ is irreducible, then the columns of **H** are simply some power α^i of a root α of $g(x)$, so that a *single* error is easily corrected because if it occurs in the $(n + 1 - i)$th column it will give a syndrome equal to α^i, and i can then be deduced from that syndrome. But if more than one error is to be corrected (which implies that $g(x)$ is composite, as we have seen), then this identification of the contributing columns of **H** from the syndrome becomes nontrivial.

However, one simple method, due to Kasami, does exist [9]. It is capable of correcting t or fewer errors in a cyclic code with distance $d = 2t + 1$, provided those errors are confined to a burst less than or equal to $(n - k)$ bits in length.

Kasami's method is based on the following reasoning. Suppose there are $j \le t$ bits in error, with r of them affecting the check digits and $(j - r)$ affecting the message bits of a systematic codeword. If we evaluate the syndrome **s**, it will have $\ge (d - (j - r))$ nonzero bits contributed from the errors in the message portion of the received vector. This is because this contribution to **s** is the remainder on dividing the message multiplied by x^{n-k} by the generating polynomial; that is, it is precisely the check digits, and since the distance of the code is d, we need $\ge (d - (j - r))$ nonzero bits. These nonzero bits may or may not cancel out the r error bits in the received check digits, which are the check digits' contribution to the syndrome. In the worst case, if all r are cancelled, the syndrome still has

$$d - (j - r) - r = d - j = 2t + 1 - j \ge t + 1$$

nonzero bits.

However, if the $j \le t$ error bits are confined to the check digits only, then the syndrome has $\le t$ nonzero bits.

If we *rotate* the received vector, we rotate a codeword plus its error pattern. Because the code is cyclic, the rotated codeword will contribute zero to the syndrome calculated from the rotated received vector. But if the error pattern is confined to $\leq (n - k)$ bits, when rotation brings it into the position of the check digits, the number of nonzero bits in the syndrome, its weight, will drop to $\leq t$, from $\geq (t + 1)$. When this occurs, the nonzero bits in the syndrome are precisely the error bits in the rotated received vector. We therefore correct them and rotate the vector back to its original position, where it is now the error-corrected codeword.

If there are $\leq t$ errors, but they are not confined to a burst of $\leq (n - k)$ bits, the syndrome will never have weight $\leq t$. The Kasami method will give no result.

If there are $> t$ errors, the error-correction procedure breaks down, as always, and could lead to erroneous error correction.

Consider, for example, the $(15, 7)$ code generated by $g(x) = x^8 + x^7 + x^6 + x^4 + 1$, with $d = 5$ and $t = 2$, which we considered in (3.3). Suppose the received vector is (111100100011111) or

$$v_0(x) = x^{14} + x^{13} + x^{12} + x^{11} + x^8 + x^4 + x^3 + x^2 + x + 1$$

Division by $g(x)$ yields a remainder syndrome

$$s_0(x) = x^6 + x^5 + x^4 + x^2 + 1$$

with weight equal to 5.

We rotate the vector left to get $v_1(x)$, which is (111001000111111), and calculate $s_1(x)$. This process is repeated to give Table 3.2.

Since, after two left rotations, the weight of $s(x) = 2 \leq t$, we conclude that the errors are

$$000000000000101$$

in $v_2(x)$ and therefore

$$010000000000001$$

Table 3.2

Rotations	$v(x)$	$s(x)$	weight of $s(x)$
0	111100100011111	01110101	5
1	111001000111111	11101010	5
2	110010001111111	00000101	2

in $v_0(x)$. Accordingly the *corrected* received vector is

$$101100100011110$$

This procedure can be simplified by noting that it is not necessary to rotate the (long) received vector. It is sufficient to rotate the syndrome, modulo $g(x)$. To see this, consider

$$s_i(x) = v_i(x) \bmod g(x)$$

Then

$$s_{i+1}(x) = (x\, v_i(x) \bmod (x^n + 1)) \bmod g(x)$$

But since $(x^n + 1)$ is divisible by $g(x)$, we have

$$s_{i+1}(x) = xv_i(x) \bmod g(x)$$
$$= xs_i(x) \bmod g(x)$$

This is illustrated in Table 3.2, where

$$s_2 = 00000101 = x^2 + 1$$

$$= xs_1(x) \bmod g(x)$$

$$= x^8 + x^7 + x^6 + x^4 + x^2 \bmod (x^8 + x^7 + x^6 + x^4 + 1)$$

When a syndrome of weight $\leq t$ is found, we rotate this back $\bmod (x^n + 1)$ (not $\bmod g(x)$) the appropriate number of times to place the error bits in the correct location for adding into the original received vector.

3.5 NONBINARY CYCLIC CODES

Cyclic codes can be constructed over $GF(q)$ where $q = p^r$ and p is prime. Multiplication is modulo $(x^n - 1)$, where n is the length of the code; and as in the binary case a cyclic code has a *monic* generating polynomial $g(x)$, with coefficients in $GF(q)$, which divides all codewords and $(x^n - 1)$. $g(x)$ is monic, that is, the coefficient of x^{n-k} is 1, to ensure the uniqueness of $g(x)$. It is, as it were, "normalised". If $g(x)$ is primitive of degree m, then $n = q^m - 1$. A primitive $g(x)$ does not give a Hamming code, because the columns of $\mathbf{H}$, which are all the powers $\alpha^i, i = 0$ to $n - 1$, of a primitive root α are not "different" since some are simply scalar multiples of others. The distance $d = 2$. For a Hamming code we require, as was shown in Chapter 2, that

$$n = (q^{n-k} - 1)/(q - 1)$$
$$= (q^m - 1)/(q - 1)$$

Provided that $(q - 1)$ is prime to this order n, the minimal polynomial of α^{q-1} (see Appendix C) will serve as a suitable generating polynomial for a Hamming code over GF(q). For an example of a nonbinary cyclic code, consider the code generated by $g(x) = x^2 + x + 2$ over GF(3).

This generating polynomial is irreducible in GF(3), and it is also primitive. Table 3.3 gives the successive powers of a primitive root α and the corresponding minimum polynomials.

Notice that although α^2 is of order $4 = (q^m - 1)/(q - 1)$ with $q = 3$ and $m = 2$, the nonprimitive $g(x) = x^2 + 1$ does not give a Hamming code.

If we introduce a factor $(x - 1)$ into a generating polynomial, the sum of all coefficients in a codeword is equal to zero. If the coefficients are over GF(2^r), this gives a longitudinal parity check on the powers of α^i, for $i = 0$ to $(r - 1)$ in the representation of GF(2^r), for the codeword elements. In general, if $g(x)$ is composite, with j irreducible polynomials over GF(q) as factors

$$n = \text{LCM}(m_i, i = 1 \text{ to } j)$$

where m_i is the order of the roots of the ith factor.

Nonbinary cyclic codes can be generated using feedback shift registers, in a manner similar to that for binary codes. Figure 3.2 illustrates this for the (8,5) example considered, over GF(3), with

$$g(x) = x^3 + x + 1 = (x^2 + x + 2)(x - 1)$$

Table 3.3

α^i	Value	Minimum Polynomial
α^0	1	$x + 2$
α^1	α	$x^2 + x + 2$
α^2	$2\alpha + 1$	$x^2 + 1$
α^3	$2\alpha + 2$	$x^2 + x + 2$
α^4	2	$x + 1$
α^5	2α	$x + 2x + 2$
α^6	$\alpha + 2$	$x^2 + 1$
α^7	$\alpha + 1$	$x^2 + 2x + 2$

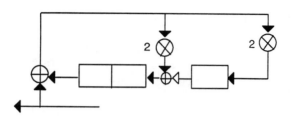

Figure 3.2 Feedback shift register for dividing by $(x^3 + x + 1)$.

Into the feedback loop are included multiplications by constants, corresponding to the (negative of the) coefficients of $g(x)$. (Note that the circuit calculates the remainder on division of the message by $g(x)$, and this is to be negated before appending to the message.)

Nonbinary cyclic codes over $GF(2^r)$, with a generating polynomial of degree m, have the ability to detect all single bursts of errors of length $\leq m$ symbols $= mr$ bits. Although the distance of such a code may be small, owing to the lack of linear independence of the columns of **H**, it can still be very useful for burst error detection. Correction of single bursts of errors can also be achieved using a nonbinary version of the Kasami method. However, if we can also achieve a large distance—and the maximum distance possible is $(n - k + 1)$, being the maximum number of nonzero terms in $g(x)$—while maintaining the cyclic nature of the code, we are then able to detect and correct random as well as bursts of errors. How this can be achieved is discussed in Chapter 4.

Chapter 4
BCH Codes

4.1 MINIMUM POLYNOMIALS

In Chapter 3 we have seen that a cyclic code is completely defined by its generating polynomial $g(x)$, which in turn is determined by its roots. We have also seen that the best hope of attaining a reasonable distance, d, without being forced to use a low coderate k/n, is that $g(x)$ should be *composite*, that is, have two or more irreducible polynomial factors. Each such factor of degree m_i contributes m_i rows to the **H** matrix, in the form of an "m_i-dimensional" sequence of powers of a root α_i (in an extension of the basic field to which the codewords belong). All the roots α_i have an order that divides n, where n is the length of the code, so that the α_i are solutions to $x^n = 1$.

The art of creating a good code is to choose the α_i in such a way that the columns of **H** have a high degree of linear independence, giving a large distance, while at the same time ensuring a good coderate with a large n in proportion to $(n - k)$, where $n - k = \Sigma m_i$.

We start this process by choosing a first root of $g(x)$, α, in an extension field $GF(q^s)$ of our basic field of coefficients $GF(q)$. For binary codes the fields are $GF(2^s)$ and $GF(2)$, respectively, and we shall confine ourselves to these for the moment. We then choose other roots in the same field but restrict ourselves to powers α^i of the first root. If α is a primitive member of $GF(2^s)$, this is no restriction.

Each of these roots α^i has a minimum polynomial $p_i(x)$, which is the polynomial with coefficients in $GF(2)$ of smallest degree m_i, which has α^i as a root. See Appendix C. The minimum polynomials are necessarily irreducible, and the full list of the roots of $p_i(x)$ is

$$\alpha^i (\alpha^i)^2 (\alpha^k)^4 \ldots (\alpha^i)^{2^{m_i-1}}$$

If the minimum polynomial of α has degree $m_1 = r$, then $(2^r - 1)$ divides $(2^s - 1)$. If the order of α is n, then n divides $(2^r - 1)$.

We have

$$n \mid (2^r - 1) \mid (2^s - 1)$$

Normally we would work with $r = s$ (there is little point in not doing so) and $n = (2^r - 1)$ for a primitive code; $n < (2^r - 1)$ for a nonprimitive code. The other powers α^i of α have orders that divide n and have minimum polynomials $p_i(x)$ of degree less than or equal to r.

As an example, consider $s = 6, 2^s - 1 = 63$. Let β be a primitive element of $GF(2^6)$, that is, a root of $x^6 + x + 1$.

1. If $\alpha = \beta^7$ then $\alpha^9 = 1$ and $x^6 + x^3 + 1$ is the minimum polynomial of α. We have $n = 9$, $(2^r - 1) = 63$, $(2^s - 1) = 63$.
2. If $\alpha = \beta^9$ then $\alpha^7 = 1$ and $x^3 + x + 1$ is the minimum polynomial of α. We have $n = 7$, $(2^r - 1) = 7$, $(2^s - 1) = 63$.
3. If $\alpha = \beta^{21}$ then $\alpha^3 = 1$ and $x^2 + x + 1$ is the minimum polynomial of α. We have $n = 3$, $(2^r - 1) = 3$, $(2^s - 1) = 63$.

As another example, consider $s = 8$, $2^s - 1 = 255$. Let β be a primitive element, that is, a root of $x^8 + x^4 + x^3 + x^2 + 1$, and consider $\alpha = \beta^{17}$. α has order 15 and minimum polynomial of degree 4, namely, $x^4 + x + 1$. α^3 has order 5 and minimum polynomial $x^4 + x^3 + x^2 + x + 1$. α^5 has order 3 and minimum polynomial $x^2 + x + 1$.

4.2 THE ROOTS OF BCH CODES

Bose-Chaudhuri-Hocquenghem (BCH) codes [10] are constructed from consecutive powers of a basic root α. Thus, $g(x)$ is constructed to have roots

$$\alpha^{m_0}, \alpha^{m_0+1}, \alpha^{m_0+2} \ldots \alpha^{m_0+m-1}$$

giving m consecutive powers of α. Often m_0 is chosen so that $m_0 = 1$; for simplicity we shall suppose that to have been done. We call these roots "consecutive roots" for short. Then if the minimum polynomial of α has degree r

$$\text{Degree}(g(x)) = \text{Degree}\left(\prod_{i=1,m} p_i(x) \right)$$

$$= \sum_{i=1,m} \text{Degree}(p_i(x))$$

$$\leq mr$$

But for all *even* values of $i, i = 2j$ say, α^{2j} and α^j are roots of the *same* polynomial $p_j(x)$. So for m even (and there is no point in considering m to be odd because α^{m+1} would appear automatically as a consecutive root) we have

$$(n - k) = \text{Degree} \, (g(x)) \leq mr/2 \tag{4.1}$$

Inequality (4.1) puts a bound on the number of check digits in a binary BCH code in terms of the degree of the basic root's minimum polynomial, r, and the number of irreducible factors of $g(x)$, m. We now show that this choice of roots (choice of factors of $g(x)$) also puts a lower bound on the code's distance, namely, $d \geq m + 1$.

Consider the null matrix

$$
\mathbf{H} = \begin{bmatrix}
\alpha^{n-1} & \alpha^{n-2} & \cdots & \alpha^2 & \alpha & 1 \\
(\alpha^2)^{n-1} & (\alpha^2)^{n-2} & \cdots & (\alpha^2)^2 & \alpha^2 & 1 \\
\cdots & \cdots & & & & \\
(\alpha^i)^{n-1} & (\alpha^i)^{n-2} & \cdots & (\alpha^i)^2 & \alpha^i & 1 \\
\cdots & \cdots & & & & \\
(\alpha^m)^{n-1} & (\alpha^m)^{n-2} & \cdots & (\alpha^m)^2 & \alpha^m & 1
\end{bmatrix}
$$

$$
= \begin{bmatrix}
\alpha^{n-1} & \alpha^{n-2} & \cdots & \alpha^2 & \alpha & 1 \\
(\alpha^{n-1})^2 & (\alpha^{n-2})^2 & \cdots & (\alpha^2)^2 & \alpha^2 & 1 \\
\cdots & \cdots & & & & \\
(\alpha^{n-1})^i & (\alpha^{n-2})^i & \cdots & (\alpha^2)^i & \alpha^i & 1 \\
\cdots & \cdots & & & & \\
(\alpha^{n-1})^m & (\alpha^{n-2})^m & \cdots & (\alpha^2)^m & \alpha^m & 1
\end{bmatrix} \tag{4.2}
$$

The determinant, D, formed from a selection of any m distinct columns of $\mathbf{H}$, corresponding to powers of α that we label $\alpha^{j1}, \alpha^{j2} \ldots \alpha^{jm}$ in the second equation for $\mathbf{H}$ in (4.2) is then

$$
D = \alpha^{j1} \alpha^{j2} \ldots \alpha^{jm} \begin{vmatrix}
1 & 1 & \cdots & 1 \\
\alpha^{j1} & \alpha^{j2} & \cdots & \alpha^{jm} \\
\hline
(\alpha^{j1})^{m-1} & (\alpha^{j2})^{m-1} & \cdots & (\alpha^{jm})^{m-1}
\end{vmatrix}
$$

$$
= \alpha^{j1} \alpha^{j2} \ldots \alpha^{jm} \Delta
$$

$$
= \prod_{i=1,m} \delta_i \Delta \quad \text{with } \delta_i = \alpha^{ji}
$$

and

$$\Delta = \begin{vmatrix} 1 & 1 & \cdots & 1 \\ \delta_1 & \delta_2 & \cdots & \delta_m \\ \cdots & \cdots & \cdots & \cdots \\ \delta_1^{m-1} & \delta_2^{m-1} & & \delta_m^{m-1} \end{vmatrix}$$

$$= \prod_{i<j\le m} (\delta_j - \delta_i)$$

That this last product evaluates to Δ can be verified by noting that, viewed as a polynomial in $\delta_k, 1 \le k \le m$, it has the correct degree $(m-1)$, the correct roots δ_i $i \ne k$ making $\Delta = 0$ when two columns are equal, and the correct coefficient for δ_k^{m-1}. But the δ_i are not equal by construction, because the powers α^i are not equal for $i < n$, since n is the order of α. Therefore, $D \ne 0$ and any selection of m columns of $\mathbf{H}$ must be linearly independent. But the distance of a linear code is equal to the minimum number of linearly dependent columns of $\mathbf{H}$. Therefore,

$$d \ge m + 1 \tag{4.3}$$

With $d = 2t + 1$ we have $t \ge m/2$, and combining this with inequality (4.1) we get

$$t \ge (n - k)/r \tag{4.4}$$

Inequality (4.4) shows clearly that a composite $g(x)$ in which r, the degree of the minimum polynomial of the basic root α, is much smaller than $(n - k)$, the degree of $g(x)$, is necessary for a large t.

It is important to note that (4.3) is an *inequality*, that is, it gives a lower bound for d. In the expression (4.2) for $\mathbf{H}$ we only considered m *consecutive* roots. In reality we know that there are nearly always other roots of the minimum polynomials of the consecutive roots, which we have not included as rows in $\mathbf{H}$ This omission does not invalidate our argument. We have seen that these other roots, being successive squares of previous roots, contribute nothing to the orthogonality of $\mathbf{H}$ with $\mathbf{G}$. Omitting them from considerations regarding the linear independence of the columns of $\mathbf{H}$ will certainly not increase the degree of linear independence but rather decrease it, so that $(m + 1)$ is a lower bound for d. Values larger than $(m + 1)$ are possible because, as stated, there are usually more than m rows in $\mathbf{H}$ if we were to write down all the roots, as opposed to just the consecutive roots.

For example the $(23, 12)$ Golay code, which has been mentioned, can be constructed from $\beta = \alpha^{89}$, where α is a primitive root of GF(2^{11}). For a BCH code we consider the minimum polynomial of β with roots

$$\beta, \beta^2, \beta^4, \beta^8, \beta^{16}, \beta^9, \beta^{18}, \beta^{13}, \beta^3, \beta^6, \beta^{12} \text{ (and } \beta^{24} = \beta \text{ again)}$$

obtained by successive squaring and remembering that $\beta^{23} = \beta^{2047} = 1$. It is clear that there are *four* consecutive roots here, $\beta, \beta^2, \beta^3, \beta^4$, so $d \geq 5$, if we simply choose for $g(x)$ the minimum polynomial of β with the eleven roots listed. This gives a $(23, 12)$ code with $d \geq 5$. However, in this particular case $d = 7$, and this can be shown by considering all the eleven rows of **H** rather than only the first four.

4.3 SOME EXAMPLES OF BCH CODES

In the following examples of BCH codes we start with a root, α, and its minimum polynomial and the resultant code and its distance. In each subsequent line we add new roots, giving rise to new minimum polynomials, and a new code (whose $g(x)$ is the product of all the preceding minimum polynomials) and the lower bound on its distance. Thus, over $GF(2^4)$ we start with α a root of the (primitive) $x^4 + x + 1$ and get Table 4.1.

Over $GF(2^5)$ with α a root of the (primitive) $x^5 + x^2 + 1$ we get Table 4.2.

In this example over $GF(2^5)$ notice that when α^7 is included as a root d increases from 7 to 11, because α^9 is already present in the third row. Similarly when α^{11} is introduced, α^{13} comes also and d again increases by 4, not 2. Notice also that the polynomials of rows 1 and 6, 2 and 4, 3 and 5 are reciprocals with $p'(x) = x^5 p(1/x)$ (where $p'(x), p(x)$ are reciprocals) and their roots can be paired α^i with $\alpha^{-i} = \alpha^{31-i}$.

If we consider $GF(2^6)$ with α as a root of the (nonprimitive) $x^6 + x^4 + x^2 + x + 1$, so that $\alpha^{21} = 1$, we get Table 4.3.

In this example, choosing a nonprimitive root as a starting point has not produced the more rapid increase in distance, which occurred in the case of the Golay code.

Table 4.1

Roots				Min. Polynomial	Code	Distance (Lower Bound)
α	α^2	α^4	α^8	$(x^4 + x + 1)$	$(15, 11)$	3
α^3	α^6	α^{12}	α^9	$(x^4 + x^3 + x^2 + x + 1)$	$(15, 7)$	5
α^5	α^{10}			$(x^2 + x + 1)$	$(15, 5)$	7
α^7	α^{14}	α^{13}	α^{11}	$(x^4 + x^3 + 1)$	$(15, 1)$	15

Table 4.2

	Roots				Min. Polynomial	Code	Distance (Lower Bound)
α	α^2	α^4	α^8	α^{16}	x^5+x^2+1	(31,26)	3
α^3	α^6	α^{12}	α^{24}	α^{17}	$x^5+x^4+x^3+x^2+1$	(31,21)	5
α^5	α^{10}	α^{20}	α^9	α^{18}	$x^5+x^4+x^2+x+1$	(31,16)	7
α^7	α^{14}	α^{28}	α^{25}	α^{19}	$x^5+x^3+x^2+x+1$	(31,11)	11
α^{11}	α^{22}	α^{13}	α^{26}	α^{21}	$x^5+x^4+x^3+x+1$	(31,6)	15
α^{15}	α^{30}	α^{29}	α^{27}	α^{23}	x^5+x^3+1	(31,1)	31

Table 4.3

	Roots					Min. Polynomial	Code	Distance (Lower Bound)
α	α^2	α^4	α^8	α^{16}	α^{11}	$x^6+x^4+x^2+x+1$	(21,15)	3
α^3	α^6	α^{12}				x^3+x+1	(21,12)	5
α^5	α^{10}	α^{20}	α^{19}	α^{17}	α^{13}	$x^6+x^5+x^4+x^2+1$	(21,6)	7
α^7	α^{14}					x^2+x+1	(21,4)	9
α^9	α^{18}	α^{15}				x^3+x^2+1	(21,1)	21

In all the above examples α^{m_0} with $m_0 = 1$ was chosen as a starting point. Inspection of the examples will show what happens if we start with $m_0 > 1$. For example, if, in the GF(2^6) example, we tried to form a $d = 7$ code with α^{10} as a starting point, it apparently cannot be done using only the first three rows, since we have $\alpha^{10}, \alpha^{11}, \alpha^{12}, \alpha^{13}$ but not α^9 or α^{14}, which implies $d = 5$. Nevertheless, the product of the minimum polynomials of the first three rows does give a $d = 7$ code. The mistake is to have looked at the wrong roots and treated the lower bound to the distance as the distance itself.

We can also take $m_0 = 0$ so that $x = 1$ is a root of $g(x)$. The effect of this is to make the number of consecutive roots odd, so that the lower bound to the distance is even. Viewed as an additional row added to **H**, it can be seen that the distance cannot be decreased; therefore, it must be increased if it goes from odd to even. For example, we can turn the $(23, 12)$ Golay code into a $(23, 11)$ even parity code by including β^0 in the list of roots given at the end of (4.2); and the distance rises from 7 to 8. (This procedure was illustrated in (3.3).)

In principle it is possible to tabulate all binary BCH codes with their corresponding distances. More usually the textbooks list the minimum polynomials of successive (odd) powers of a basic root in GF(2^s) for values of s from 2 to 20 or 30. These minimum polynomials are of course all the irreducible polynomials that divide $(x^{2^s-1} - 1)$.

4.4 ERROR CORRECTION OF BINARY BCH CODES

The regular structure of BCH codes given by the m "consecutive roots" enables a minimum distance, $d = 2t + 1 = m + 1$, to be determined. This structure also permits correction of up to t errors to be performed by a relatively simple procedure.

Suppose we have t errors and evaluate syndromes S_i by multiplying the received vector into the columns of $\mathbf{H}^T$, that is, the rows of $\mathbf{H}$. For a BCH code these rows include

$$(\alpha^i)^{n-1}(\alpha^i)^{n-2}\ldots(\alpha^i)^2(\alpha^i)1$$

for $i = m_0$ to $(m_0 + m - 1)$ if there are m consecutive roots. The rows can also be written

$$(\alpha^{n-1})^i(\alpha^{n-2})^i\ldots(\alpha^2)^i(\alpha)^i(1)^i$$

for $i = m_0$ to $(m_0 + m - 1)$.

Errors in columns corresponding to $\alpha^{j1}, \alpha^{j2}, \ldots \alpha^{jt}$ will then give rise to syndromes

$$S_i = (\alpha^{j1})^i + (\alpha^{j2})^i \ldots + (\alpha^{jt})^i$$

We write $\alpha^{jk} = X_k$ and call this an *error locator*, because if we know the value of X_k we know the column in $\mathbf{H}$ to which it belongs and hence the location of the error. Thus,

$$S_i = \sum_{k=1,t} X_k^i \quad \text{for } i = m_0 \ \text{ to } (m_0 + m - 1) \tag{4.5}$$

S_i is found from the received vector, and there are $m = 2t$ nonlinear equations in (4.5) to find the t values X_k for $k = 1$ to t. However, the system (4.5) is not overdetermined, since some equations are simply restatements of others. This is clearly seen if we take $m_0 = 1$, in which case $S_{2j} = S_j^2$ for $j = 1$ to $m/2$. Equations (4.5) can be solved by turning the nonlinear into a linear system, as follows.

Suppose the X_i are the t roots of an equation

$$f(x) = x^t + f_1 x^{t-1} \ldots + f_{t-1} x + f_t = 0 \tag{4.6}$$

Then

$$X_i^t + f_1 X_i^{t-1} \ldots + f_{t-1} X_i + f_t = 0 \tag{4.7}$$

Multiplying (4.7) by X_i^j, with $1 \leq j \leq t$, and summing over $i = 1$ to t gives

$$S_{t+j} + f_1 S_{t+j-1} \cdots + f_{t-1} S_{j+1} + f_t S_j = 0 \tag{4.8}$$

Equations (4.8) (the "Newton identities") are t linear equations, for $j = 1$ to t, which enable the t coefficients f_1 to f_t to be calculated, and hence the X_i to be found by solving (4.6).

Thus, the error-correction procedure for BCH codes is

1. Find the $m = 2t$ syndromes corresponding to the consecutive roots.
2. Solve the linear system of t equations (4.8) to find the coefficients f_1 to f_t.
3. Solve (4.6) to find the t error locators X_i.
4. Determine the columns in **H** where errors have occurred from the values X_i and change the bits in the received vector corresponding to those columns.

4.4.1 Practical Procedures for Solving the Equations

Various methods have been developed for speeding up the calculations in steps 2 and 3; but given that in most cases t is relatively small (e.g., $t < 10$) and that computers are being used in any case, simple direct methods often are sufficient.

Thus, step 2 may be performed by normal methods for linear equations (e.g., determinants) without taking into account the "diagonal" arrangement of the S_1 to S_{2t} or the fact that there are only $2t$ rather than t^2 distinct matrix elements. And in step 3 there are only n possible values for the X_i, namely α^0 to $\alpha^{(n-1)}$, and these can simply be tested one by one to see if they are roots of $f(x)$.

However, it is important to note that if the number of errors is $r < t$ then $f(x)$ is only of degree r and the system of equations (4.8) becomes singular. This presents problems in step 2. More precisely, if there are $r, 0 < r < t$, errors and we assume that there are $s, 0 < s \leq t$, errors and therefore use a function $f(x)$ of degree s, the system of equations (4.8) is effectively insoluble unless we guess $s = r$ correctly. To understand how this is so, consider the situation when there are $r(\leq t)$ real errors.

Equations (4.8) then become

$$S_{j+r} = f_1 S_{j+r-1} \cdots + f_{r-1} S_{j+1} + f_r S_j \tag{4.9}$$

for $1 \leq j \leq 2t - r$, since $f(x)$ is now only of degree r, but the number of syndromes evaluated is $2t$. This system of $(2t - r)$ equations in r unknown is either inconsistent or else contains redundant (linearly dependent) equations. It cannot be inconsistent, because it is true; therefore, the excess $(2t - r - r = 2t - 2r)$ equations must be satisfied automatically by the solution to the first r equations. The matrix associated with those first r equations, namely,

$$(S_{j+r-1}S_{j+r-2}\ldots S_{j+1}S_j) \qquad j=1 \quad \text{to } r$$

is nonsingular, because if it were singular we could choose one variable (f_r, say) in (4.9) arbitrarily, and choosing $f_r = 0$ would imply $X_i = 0$ for some $1 \le i \le r$, which contradicts the assumption that there are r errors. Therefore, if the number of errors we guess to be present, s, equals the number of errors really present, r, then (4.9) can always be solved, with $1 \le r \le t$. However, if we guess $s < r$, then we cannot find solutions f_i to

$$0 = S_{j+s} + f_1'S_{j+s-1} + \ldots f_{s-1}''S_{j+1} + f_s'S_j \qquad (4.10)$$

for $1 \le j \le 2t - s$, because all $(s + 1)$ by $(s + 1)$ matrices, formed from the rows

$$(S_{j+s}S_{j+s-1}\ldots S_{j+1}S_j)$$

for $(s + 1)$ differing values of j, would then have to be singular for the homogeneous set (4.10) to be true. But if all these matrices are singular (with $s < r$), then the determinant of the right side of (4.9) is zero, which contradicts the fact that there are nonzero solutions to (4.9). Therefore, when $s < r$, (4.10) is insoluble and represents an inconsistent set of equations. If we guess $s < r$ and find f_1' to f_s' from the first s equations, they will not satisfy the remaining $(2t - 2s)$ equations.

Finally, if we guess $s < r$, we cannot solve (4.10) for f_i' ($i = 1$ to s), because the matrix

$$(S_{j+s-1}S_{j+s-2}\ldots S_{j+1}S_j) \qquad \text{for } j = 1 \text{ to } s \qquad (4.11)$$

is *singular*, because all $(r \cdot r)$ determinants of the homogeneous system (4.9)

$$(S_{j+r}S_{j+r-1}\ldots S_{j+1}S_j)$$

for any r values of j, $1 \le j \le 2t - r$, are zero; which makes the determinant of (4.11) equal to zero.

Thus, we conclude that in step 2 the way to proceed is to guess that there are $s = t$ errors. If the matrix of (4.8) $(S_{s+j-1}S_{s+j-2}S_{j+1}S_j)$ for $j = 1$ to s is nonsingular, solve (4.8) for f_1 to f_s and proceed to step 3. If the matrix is singular, decrement s and try again for a nonsingular matrix. When a solution is found, it can be checked for consistency in the last $(2t - 2s)$ equations:

$$S_{s+j} + f_1 S_{s+j-1} \ldots + f_{s-1}S_{j+1} + f_s S_j = 0 \quad \text{with} \quad j = (s+1) \text{ to } (2t-s)$$

4.4.2 An Example of BCH Error Correction

To illustrate the method, consider the $(15, 5)$ code listed in (4.3) with

$$g(x) = (x^4 + x + 1)(x^4 + x^3 + x^2 + x + 1)(x^2 + x + 1) \quad \text{and} \quad d = 7$$

The code is capable of correcting three errors, but suppose only two occur, namely,

$$001000010000000$$

Then consecutive roots are $\alpha, \alpha^2, \alpha^3, \alpha^4, \alpha^5, \alpha^6$ with an α root of $x^4 + x + 1$. We evaluate syndromes S_1, S_3, and S_5 directly and then calculate S_2, S_4, and S_6 by squaring. With

$$\mathbf{H} = \begin{bmatrix} \alpha^{14} & \alpha^{13} & \alpha^{12} & \alpha^{11} & \alpha^{10} & \alpha^9 & \alpha^8 & \alpha^7 & \alpha^6 & \alpha^5 & \alpha^4 & \alpha^3 & \alpha^2 & \alpha & 1 \\ \alpha^{12} & \alpha^9 & \alpha^6 & \alpha^3 & 1 & \alpha^{12} & \alpha^9 & \alpha^6 & \alpha^3 & 1 & \alpha^{12} & \alpha^9 & \alpha^6 & \alpha^3 & 1 \\ \alpha^{10} & \alpha^5 & 1 & \alpha^{10} & \alpha^5 & 1 & \alpha^{10} & \alpha^5 & 1 & \alpha^{10} & \alpha^5 & 1 & \alpha^{10} & \alpha^5 & 1 \end{bmatrix}$$

we get

$$S_1 = \alpha^{12} + \alpha^7 = \alpha^2$$

$$S_2 = S_1^2 = \alpha^4$$

$$S_3 = \alpha^6 + \alpha^6 = 0$$

$$S_4 = S_2^2 = \alpha^8$$

$$S_5 = 1 + \alpha^5 = \alpha^{10}$$

$$S_6 = S_3^2 = 0$$

Table 4.4 lists the powers of α, where $\alpha^4 + \alpha + 1 = 0$ has been used.
To solve

$$S_{3+j} + f_1 S_{2+j} + f_2 S_{1+j} + f_3 S_j = 0$$

with $j = 1, 2, 3$ (on the assumption that there are *three* errors), we need to evaluate

Table 4.4

	α^0	α^1	α^2	α^3	α^4	α^5	α^6	α^7	α^8	α^9	α^{10}	α^{11}	α^{12}	α^{13}	α^{14}
α^3	0	0	0	1	0	0	1	1	0	1	0	1	1	1	1
α^2	0	0	1	0	0	1	1	0	1	0	1	1	1	1	0
α	0	1	0	0	1	1	0	1	0	1	1	1	1	0	0
1	1	0	0	0	1	0	0	1	1	0	1	0	1	1	1

the determinant

$$\begin{vmatrix} S_3 S_2 S_1 \\ S_4 S_3 S_2 \\ S_5 S_4 S_3 \end{vmatrix} = \begin{vmatrix} 0 & \alpha^4 & \alpha^2 \\ \alpha^8 & 0 & \alpha^4 \\ \alpha^{10} & \alpha^8 & 0 \end{vmatrix} = 0$$

This shows that there are fewer than three errors, so we try again with

$$S_{2+j} + f_1 S_{1+j} + f_2 S_j = 0 \qquad (4.12)$$

with $j = 1$ to 4. Considering only $j = 1, 2$ first, we find the determinant

$$D = \begin{vmatrix} S_2 & S_1 \\ S_3 & S_2 \end{vmatrix} \quad \begin{vmatrix} \alpha^4 & \alpha^2 \\ 0 & \alpha^4 \end{vmatrix} = \alpha^8$$

So that

$$f_1 = \begin{vmatrix} S_3 & S_1 \\ S_4 & S_2 \end{vmatrix} / D = \alpha^{10}/\alpha^8 = \alpha^2$$

$$f_2 = \begin{vmatrix} S_2 & S_3 \\ S_3 & S_4 \end{vmatrix} / D = \alpha^{12}/\alpha^8 = \alpha^4$$

This means that the error locators X_1, X_2 are roots of $(x^2 + \alpha^2 x + \alpha^4)$, and it is easy to verify that α^7 and α^{12} are these roots, pinpointing the errors to be

$$(001000010000000)$$

We verify the remaining equations of (4.12) with $j = 3, 4$, namely,

$$S_5 + f_1 S_4 + f_2 S_3 = \alpha^{10} + \alpha^{10} + 0 = 0$$
$$S_6 + f_1 S_5 + f_2 S_4 = 0 + \alpha^{12} + \alpha^{12} = 0$$

Finally, if we had guessed that there was only *one* error we would have solved

$$S_2 + f_1 S_1 = 0$$

to give $f_1 = \alpha^2$. But if we try to verify this for the remaining equations $S_{j+1} + f_1 S_j = 0$ with $j = 2$ to 5, we get

$$S_3 + f_1 S_2 = 0 + \alpha^6 \neq 0$$
$$S_4 + f_1 S_3 = \alpha^8 + 0 \neq 0$$
$$S_5 + f_1 S_4 = \alpha^{10} + \alpha^{10} = 0$$
$$S_6 + f_1 S_5 = 0 + \alpha^{12} \neq 0$$

showing clearly that the equations are inconsistent, because there are *two*, not one, errors.

This procedure for step 2 is based on trial and error, with $1 \le r \le t$. In many practical cases t is small, so there is not much superfluous effort wasted in finding the r that gives a nonsingular matrix in (4.9) and consistent results for the remaining $2(t - r)$ equations. However, there exists an ingenious and faster method for solving these equations (due to Berlekamp and Massey) that automatically determines the number of errors r as it proceeds to find the f_i for $i = 1$ to r. Essentially the method relies on the fact that (4.9),

$$S_{j+r} = f_1 S_{j+r-1} + f_2 S_{j+r-2} \cdots + f_{r-1} S_{j+1} + f_r S_j$$

may be regarded as a linear predictor of S_{j+r}, given S_{j+r-1} to S_j, with coefficients f_1 to f_r. The Berlekamp-Massey algorithm [11] synthesises such a linear predictor by predicting S_2 from S_1; S_3 from S_2, S_1; S_4 from S_3, S_2, S_1, and so on, modifying coefficients up to f_r as necessary. When the algorithm has found f_1 to f_r that predict S_{r+1} correctly (from S_r to S_1), it transpires that S_{r+2} can be predicted without adding an f_{r+1} coefficient, so the S_1 term is dropped. The algorithm continues until S_{2t} is predicted, but these later stages merely verify that the r found is indeed correct and the $f_i, i = 1$ to r, are the coefficients of $f(x)$. The algorithm is presented in Appendix D.

4.5 ERROR CORRECTION OF NONBINARY BCH CODES

A technique very similar to that of (4.4) can be used to find and correct errors in nonbinary BCH codes. Nonbinary BCH codes are simply nonbinary cyclic codes, as discussed in Section 3.5, with the added requirement that there are m consecutive powers of a basic root α (in an extension field to GF(q), the field of the coefficients and the code itself) as roots of the generating polynomial $g(x)$.

Because the coefficients of the code polynomials are not restricted to 0 or 1, the syndrome equation (4.5) now becomes

$$S_i = \sum_k Y_k X_k^i \quad i = m_0 \text{ to } (m_0 + m - 1) \tag{4.13}$$

where Y_k is the *value* of the kth error, at the location identified by X_k. As before, the nonlinear equations in X_k of (4.13) are transformed to linear ones by supposing the X_k are roots of $f(x)$, of degree t, so that

$$f(X_k) = X_k^t + f_1 X_k^{t-1} \cdots + f_{t-1} X_k + f_t = 0$$

But this time we multiply not merely by X_k^j, but by $Y_k X_k^j$ and sum over k to get, using (4.13),

$$S_{j+t} + f_1 S_{j+t-1} + f_2 S_{j+t-2} \cdots + f_{t-1} S_{j+1} + f_t S_j = 0$$

This can be solved as before for the f_i, $i = 1$ to t, to give the $f(x)$, whose roots in turn can be found to give the X_k. Equation (4.13) is then a system of linear equations in Y_k, with S_i and X_k^i known, which can be solved to give the error values.

The process can be summarised as follows:

1. Evaluate the syndromes S_i for $i = 1$ to $2t$. They will satisfy (4.13), that is,
   $S_i = \sum_{k=1,t} Y_k X_k^i$
2. Find the coefficients f_i of $f(x)$, the polynomial with the error locators as roots, by solving $S_{j+t} + f_1 S_{j+t-1} + f_2 S_{j+i-2} \cdots + f_{t-1} S_{j+1} + f_t S_j = 0$ for $j = 1$ to t or shortened versions of this if there are fewer than t errors.
3. Find the error locators that are the roots X_k of $f(x)$. If $X_k = \alpha^{k_i}$, then the error is in the $(n - k_i)^{\text{th}}$ position of the codevector, reading from the left.
4. Evaluate the Y_k from $\sum_{k=1,t} Y_k X_k^i$ by matrix inversion and subtract them from the received vector at the appropriate locations identified by the X_k.

The above procedure is quite simple to implement, although the manipulation of two finite fields the ground field GF(q) and the extension field of the roots, in which powers of the basic root will be represented as polynomial remainders on division by the minimal (nonbinary) polynomial of the basic root can become confusing. Fortunately the classic nonbinary BCH codes, the Reed-Solomon codes, require only one nonbinary field.

4.6 REED-SOLOMON (RS) CODES

Reed-Solomon codes [12] are remarkably simple, despite being nonbinary BCH codes over a ground field GF(q). As with all BCH codes m consecutive roots are chosen, but the roots are in the ground field itself, not in an extension of it. Thus, if the basic root is α (in GF(q)), the other roots are α^i, and all have minimum polynomials of degree equal to unity, $(x - a^i)$. Thus, the generating polynomial is

$$g(x) = \prod(x - \alpha^i)$$

We have $(n - k) = m$; and $d = m + 1 = n - k + 1$ for the distance. Notice that this is the maximum possible value for d since there are only $(n - k)$ rows in $\mathbf{H}$; therefore, any $(n - k + 1)$ columns of $\mathbf{H}$ are linearly dependent. The *length* of an RS code is given by $n = q - 1$ because $\alpha^{q-1} = 1$, since the order of α certainly divides $(q - 1)$. But α is always chosen to be primitive, because no advantage accrues from using a nonprimitive α, given that the distance is maximum in any case. If a shorter length is required, it is simpler to use a shortened RS code, which will also have $d = n - k + 1$ for the same reason.

4.6.1 A Worked RS Example

It is usually convenient to choose $m_0 = 0$ for the sequence of roots $\alpha^{m_0}, \alpha^{m_0+1} \dots \alpha^{m_0+m-1}$, and this is done in the following example. First we construct a $d = 5$ RS code over GF(2^3), and then we use it to correct two symbol errors in accordance with the procedure of (4.5). Let the roots be $1, \alpha, \alpha^2, \alpha^3$, where α is primitive in GF(2^3), for example, α is a root of $x^3 + x + 1$. This gives

$$\alpha^3 = \alpha + 1, \alpha^4 = \alpha^2 + \alpha, \alpha^5 = \alpha^2 + \alpha + 1, \alpha^6 = \alpha^2 + 1$$

So that $g(x)$
$$= (x + 1)(x + \alpha)(x + \alpha^2)(x + \alpha^3)$$
$$= (x^2 + \alpha^3 x + \alpha)(x^2 + \alpha^5 x + \alpha^5)$$
$$= x^4 + \alpha^2 x^3 + \alpha^5 x^2 + \alpha^5 x + \alpha^6$$

This gives a (7, 3) RS code over GF(2^3) with $d = n - k + 1 = 5$.

$$G = \begin{bmatrix} 1 & 0 & 0 & \alpha & \alpha^3 & \alpha^6 & \alpha^6 \\ 0 & 1 & 0 & 1 & \alpha^4 & \alpha^2 & \alpha \\ 0 & 0 & 1 & \alpha^2 & \alpha^5 & \alpha^5 & \alpha^6 \end{bmatrix}$$

$$H = \begin{bmatrix} \alpha & 1 & \alpha^2 & 1 & 0 & 0 & 0 \\ \alpha^3 & \alpha^4 & \alpha^5 & 0 & 1 & 0 & 0 \\ \alpha^6 & \alpha^2 & \alpha^5 & 0 & 0 & 1 & 0 \\ \alpha^6 & \alpha & \alpha^6 & 0 & 0 & 0 & 1 \end{bmatrix}$$

H can also be represented in a form showing the powers of the roots

$$H = \begin{bmatrix} 1 & 1 & 1 & 1 & 1 & 1 & 1 \\ \alpha^6 & \alpha^5 & \alpha^4 & \alpha^3 & \alpha^2 & \alpha & 1 \\ \alpha^5 & \alpha^3 & \alpha & \alpha^6 & \alpha^4 & \alpha^2 & 1 \\ \alpha^4 & \alpha & \alpha^5 & \alpha^2 & \alpha^6 & \alpha^3 & 1 \end{bmatrix}$$

by adding together suitable multiples of the rows of the first form of H.

We can represent the elements of $GF(2^3)$ as triplets $(\alpha^2 \alpha 1)$ so that (101) signifies $\alpha^2 + 1 = \alpha^6$. Then a codeword could be

$$(1 \ \alpha \ 0 \ 0 \ \alpha^2 \ \alpha^4 \ 1) = (001 \ 010 \ 000 \ 000 \ 100 \ 110 \ 001)$$

We suppose this becomes corrupted to

$$(001 \ 010 \ 111 \ 000 \ 101 \ 110 \ 001)$$
$$= (1 \ \alpha \ \alpha^5 \ 0 \ \alpha^6 \ \alpha^4 \ 1)$$

and we get the following syndromes

$$S_1 = 1 + \alpha + \alpha^5 + \alpha^6 + \alpha^4 + 1 = \alpha^2 + \alpha = \alpha^4$$
$$S_2 = \alpha^6 + \alpha^6 + \alpha^2 + 0 + \alpha + \alpha^5 + 1 = 0$$
$$S_3 = \alpha^5 + \alpha^4 + \alpha^6 + 0 + \alpha^3 + \alpha^6 + 1 = \alpha + 1 = \alpha^3$$
$$S_4 = \alpha^4 + \alpha^2 + \alpha^3 + 0 + \alpha^5 + 1 + 1 = \alpha^2 + \alpha = \alpha^4$$

On the assumption that there are two errors we try to solve for f_1 and f_2

$$S_3 = f_1 S_2 + f_2 S_1$$
$$S_4 = f_1 S_3 + f_2 S_2$$

The determinant $= S_2^2 - S_1 S_3 = 0 + \alpha^7 = 1$ and we get

$$f_1 = \begin{vmatrix} S_3 S_1 \\ S_4 S_2 \end{vmatrix} = S_3 S_2 + S_4 S_1$$

$$= 0 + \alpha^8 = \alpha$$

$$f_2 = \begin{vmatrix} S_2 S_3 \\ S_3 S_4 \end{vmatrix} = S_2 S_4 + S_3^2$$

$$= 0 + \alpha^6 = \alpha^6$$

The error locators are found by solving

$$f(x) = x^2 + f_1 x + f_2 = 0$$

giving roots $x = \alpha^2$ and $x = \alpha^4$, so the errors have been located in the $(7 - 4) = $ 3rd and $(7 - 2) = $ 5th positions from the left. The *values* of the errors are given by

$$Y_1 + Y_2 = S_1 = \alpha^4$$
$$\alpha^4 Y_1 + \alpha^2 Y_2 = S_2 = 0$$

giving

$$Y_2 = \alpha^2 Y_1$$

so

$$Y_1 = \alpha^4/(1 + \alpha^2) = \alpha^4/\alpha^6 = \alpha^5$$

Therefore,

$$Y_1 = \alpha^5 \qquad Y_2 = \alpha^7 = 1$$
$$= (111) \qquad\qquad = (001)$$

which added back into

$$(001 \quad 010 \quad 111 \quad 000 \quad 101 \quad 110 \quad 001)$$

as follows,

$$(000 \quad 000 \quad 111 \quad 000 \quad 001 \quad 000 \quad 000)$$

gives the original vector,

$$(001 \quad 010 \quad 000 \quad 000 \quad 100 \quad 110 \quad 001)$$

4.6.2 An Example of Practical Use of RS Codes

The preceding example illustrated the calculations involved in error correction based on an RS code. The following example is of an *application* using an RS code. The application is the transmission by radio (spare capacity on a satellite TV channel in reality) of blocks of broadcast financial data. The one-to-many nature of broadcasting and the relatively noisy transmission medium make the application a natural candidate for FEC, as opposed to correction by retransmission.

The data are composed of blocks of 36 octets (bytes), transmitted between framing characters (which do not concern us) and forming a series of perhaps 200 or 300 blocks. Because the receiving radio equipment may temporarily lose synchronisation with the framing, every so often (e.g., one block in a few hundred) an *entire* 36-octet block may be destroyed. This erroneous block may sometimes be signalled as such, but usually it is not; the application could then be fed with 36 arbitrary but apparently genuine octets. Random single bit errors also occasionally occur.

To provide error correction for this application it was decided to use interleaved shortened RS codes over $GF(2^8)$. The scheme is illustrated in Figure 4.1. The columns represent codewords, which for an RS code over $GF(2^8)$ must have $n \leq 255$. In practice a distance-5 RS code was used with roots $1, \alpha, \alpha^2, \alpha^3$, where α is a (primitive) root of $x^8 + x^5 + x^3 + x + 1$, giving

$$g(x) = x^4 + \alpha^{219}x^3 + \alpha^{56}x^2 + \alpha^{222}x + \alpha^6$$

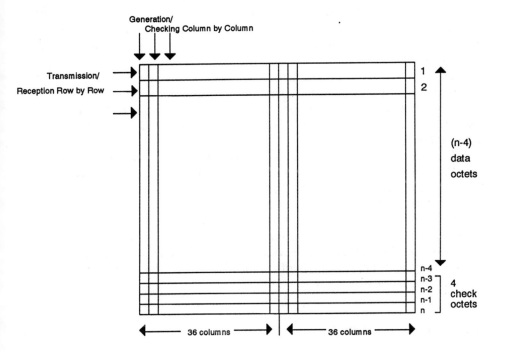

* On transmission, first the columns are filled, then the rows transmitted

* On reception, first the rows are received, then the columns checked

Figure 4.1 Example of interleaved RS code.

Thus each column has ≤ 251 data octets and four *check digit* octets. Seventy-two columns, representing two transmission blocks, were chosen.

The *interleaving* is achieved by filling the matrix column by column. As soon as $(n-4)$ octets are read in, the four check digits are calculated and added to the bottom of the current column, and the process continues on the next column. But once all columns are full, transmission starts by sending out octets *row by row*. Thus, the 72 leading octets of each column are sent as the first two transmission blocks, then the 72 second octets, and so on. On reception the rows are filled in the same way as they were emptied on transmission, and then RS error correction proceeds *column by column*. It is clear that two completely corrupted 36-octet transmission blocks cannot cause more than two octet errors in an RS codeword, and the likelihood is that they will usually cause fewer. Thus, two blocks in error in $2n$ blocks are correctable, with $n \leq 255$ and $k = n - 4$.

The choice of $GF(2^8)$ was made partly because of the ease of handling octet-based operations, and partly because the maximum value for n ($= 255$) suited the requirements for the application to handle a series of "a few hundred 36-octet transmission blocks".

The interleaving technique described above is a very simple technique for turning bursts of errors (e.g., a 36-octet block) into random errors. The RS code enables these and other random octet and bit errors to be corrected readily and has the merit of adapting itself to various lengths $n(\leq 255)$ without change of distance $d(= 5)$.

Thus, the system can be and is configured to meet differing requirements from the application, in terms of number of blocks in a series, and to adapt to differing error rates, by adjusting the length of the code and so changing the probability of an octet in a codeword being in error.

In many radio-based broadcast transmission systems the entire digital stream, framing characters and so forth included, is itself error-corrected using a convolutional code (see Chapter 5); so if block coding is used within the stream, two levels of error correction apply. This is often called concatenated coding, because one coder follows another as the data are processed.

4.6.3 Other Aspects of RS Codes

Some final comments on RS codes can be made. First, the *weight distribution* of RS codes can be readily calculated, and this enables the probability of correct and incorrect decoding and of other parameters such as the postdecoding error rate (the *residual error rate*) to be calculated accurately, as has been indicated.

The calculation of the weight distribution relies on the fact that the contents of any k symbol positions, over all q^k codewords of an RS code, are all distinct. This is because if two codewords had equal values in those k positions, they could be subtracted to form a codeword with zero in those postions; therefore, with $d \le n - k$. But $d = n - k + 1$, so this is possible only if the result is the all-zero codeword, in which case the codewords were not distinct in the first place.

Applying this to a consideration of the number of codewords of weight $= d = n - k + 1$, we can see that for any d positions a codeword of weight $= d$ exists. For an example, consider $(d\text{-}1)$ of these positions leaving $n - (n - k) = k$ over. All q^k values occur in these k positions when all q^k codewords are considered; therefore, in particular the codeword with all zeros, except for 1 in the dth postion of those originally considered, occurs. But this must have weight $= d$; therefore, the remaining $(d - 1)$ postions are nonzero; therefore we have a codeword of weight d. There are $\binom{n}{d} (q - 1)$ such codewords of weight d, because there are $\binom{n}{d}$ selected positions possible, and for each codeword there is a possible scalar multiplication by $(q - 1)$.

It is interesting to consider "how good" are RS codes, given that the distance $d = n - k + 1$ is maximum (given n, k) and that $k/n = 1 - 2t/n$ for large n. This means that the coderate is preserved if t/n is preserved as n increases, and vice versa. But how near the theoretical bounds are RS codes?

From Appendix B we have

$$\sum_{i=0, n\alpha} \binom{n}{i} < 2^n H(\alpha)$$

for large n; therefore, the summation term in the inequality of Section 2.5, which is applicable to the nonbinary sphere-packing case, can certainly be bounded as follows:

$$\sum_{i=0, n\alpha} \binom{n}{i} (q - 1)^i < 2^{nH(\alpha)}(q - 1)^{n\alpha} < 2^{nH(\alpha)} q^{n\alpha}$$

In consequence, the sphere-packing bound with $\alpha = t/n$ becomes

$$M = q^k < q^n / 2^{nH(\alpha)} q^{n\alpha}$$

Taking logarithms to the base q we get

$$\text{Coderate} = k/n < (1 - \alpha - H(\alpha)/m) \tag{4.14}$$

where we have assumed $q = m$ so that $\log_q 2 = 1/m$. (It must also be remembered that since in the case of RS codes $n = q - 1$, $m \sim \log_2 n$ so that $H(\alpha)/m$ tends to zero as n becomes very large.) The Plotkin bound of Chapter 2 can also be recalculated for the nonbinary case to give

$$\text{Coderate} = k/n \leq 1 - q(2t+1)/(q-1) - \log_q(q-1)/n$$

which for large n may be approximated by

$$\text{Coderate} = k/n \leq 1 - 2\alpha q/(q-1) \tag{4.15}$$

For large q (as occurs with RS codes)

$$k/n \leq 1 - 2\alpha \tag{4.16}$$

and we see that the Plotkin bound (4.15), which takes into account the code's linearity, is considerably more constraining than the (in any case conservative) sphere-packing bound of (4.14).

Reed-Solomon codes attain this upper Plotkin bound (4.16), as we have seen. How near are RS codes to the theoretical limits as given by Shannon's theorem of Section 1.3? The theorem puts a bound on the coderate, which can be achieved with arbitrarily small probability of decoding error. For such a probability, the correctable errors must at least include the expected number of errors Pn, where P is the probability of a symbol error. Therefore, $t \geq Pn$

For RS codes with $\alpha = t/n$ this implies

$$k/n \leq 1 - 2P \tag{4.17}$$

But Shannon's theorem states that

$$k/n \leq 1 - H(p) \tag{4.18}$$

where p is the bit-error probability. If $q = 2^m$ then each symbol is represented by m bits and the symbol-error probability is related to the bit-error probability by

$$P = \left(1 - (1-p)^m\right) \tag{4.19}$$

It is clear that as n increases, thereby increasing $m = \log_2(n+1)$, the probability of a symbol error P increases to reach (and exceed) $1/2$, so that the coderate of the RS code given by (4.17) decreases to zero, until finally no RS codes of the required characteristics exist. This situation is far less favourable than the theoretical coderate given by (4.18).

In short, the good performance of RS codes with large n as evidenced by their attainment of the Plotkin bound (4.16) is in fact an illusion. It is achieved by considering symbols requiring ever more bits m to represent them, so that if used on a channel of fixed bit-error probability p, the symbol-error probability P

increases with n. We may maintain the ratio t/n, but we *should increase it* to cope with the increasing P, as n increases. If we do this using (4.17) with P given by (4.19), the coderate drops away from the theoretical limit of (4.18). Because RS codes are at the Plotkin bound, it is clear that this limitation on performance is essentially due to the *linearity* of the code.

Despite these strictures, RS codes are very useful, not least because they have built-in burst-error detection and correction (being nonbinary); and because they require only relatively straightforward calculations for error correction.

Chapter 5
Convolutional Codes

5.1 TREE AND TRELLIS CODES

The previous chapters have been concerned with block codes, in which information symbols are supplemented with check digits, symbols, and bits, which create the distance between codewords and enable error detection and correction to be performed. The check digits are calculated from the information symbols in the block. The block is self-sufficient.

This chapter is concerned with streams of blocks, usually very short in length, supplemented with check digits that are calculated from the information symbols of the current block *and of several preceding blocks*. While the number of information and check digits per block is known and is a fixed property of the code in use, the number of blocks in the stream is usually indeterminate and considered to be infinite. In general these codes need not even be systematic, so that a block in the stream is simply a collection of v symbols derived from, but not necessarily containing the input b information symbols, to give a coderate b/v. The important difference between these codes and block codes lies in the fact that *successive blocks are interdependent*.

Viewed in another way we may consider *tree codes*, the most general form of such codes, to be generated by a state-changing process. In this process, the code generator moves from one state to a new state as determined by the input symbols, the symbols to be encoded, and on each transition between states it emits output symbols, which depend on the input symbols and on the state from which the transition is made. Thus, from a given state, possible paths (depending on the sequence of input symbols) spread out like the branches of a tree; each path is associated with a sequence of output symbols, which form the transmitted (infinite) codevector. The recipient of the codevector must try to recreate the sequence of input symbols, and to be able to do this in the presence of transmission errors clearly requires the existence of some distance properties between codevectors.

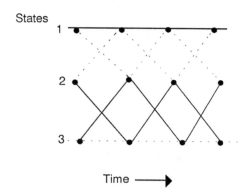

Figure 5.1 A 3-state 2-input trellis.

In practice such code trees do not spread out indefinitely. There exists only a *finite number of states*, usually determined by the last $(k-1)$ groups of b symbols, where k is known as the *constraint length* and includes the current input symbols. If we regard the states as m points on a vertical line and time (measured in transition intervals) as increasing horizontally to the right, the code can be represented as a *trellis* in which each state connects to j other states in the vertical line to the right of it, as determined by the j possible values for the input symbols causing the transition. After n transitions there are mj^n possible paths through the trellis, and the decoder's job is to determine *which* of these was taken by examining the output symbols emitted on each transition. If the input and output symbols are binary, we typically have $m = 2^{b(k-1)}$, $j = 2^b$.

A simple trellis code is illustrated in Figure 5.1, with $m = 3$ and $j = 2$. Numbering the states 1, 2, 3 and denoting the input symbols by 0 and 1, we could define the coding procedure for generating the output symbols as

On each transition, output the state number followed by the input symbol.

The state transition rules themselves are defined by the diagram with continuous lines corresponding to transitions caused by input 0, dashed lines caused by input 1.

Thus (starting in state 1), input 101101000 gives output 112031313021101010.

5.1.1 The Viterbi Algorithm

Trellis codes can be decoded with the *Viterbi algorithm* [13]. The basis of this algorithm is that, in seeking the codevector **c** nearest to a received vector **r**, it is not necessary to compare every possible $\mathbf{c}$ with $\mathbf{r}$. It is sufficient to maintain for each state i ($i = 1, m$) that codevector that is nearest to $\mathbf{r}$ and that terminates at state i. We denote this codevector, at instant n, by $\mathbf{c}_{i,n}$. Now when the next v symbols are received, corresponding to the extension of $\mathbf{r}_n$ to $\mathbf{r}_{(n+1)}$, the distance between $\mathbf{c}_{i,(n+1)}$ and $\mathbf{r}_{(n+1)}$ is the minimum distance between $\mathbf{c}_{p,n}$ and $\mathbf{r}_n$ (where $\mathbf{c}_p$ is the codevector leading to state p, a predecessor of state i) plus the distance between the new v symbols received and those that would be emitted in the transition p to i; with minimisation taking place with respect to p.

$$\text{Minimum Distance } (\mathbf{c}_{i,(n+1)}, \mathbf{r}_{(n+1)})$$

$$= \text{Min}\left[d(\mathbf{c}_{p,n}, \mathbf{r}_n) + d(\mathbf{r}_n \rightarrow \mathbf{r}_{(n+1)}, \mathbf{c}_{p,n} \rightarrow \mathbf{c}_{i,n+1}) \right]$$

(The arrow $\rightarrow$ indicates that the symbols associated with the transfer are to be used.)

Thus, the algorithm proceeds by finding the new path to state i, nearest to $\mathbf{r}$, by minimising the distance over i's preceding states p. Accordingly in the one operation the nearest distance is found *and the path through the trellis*, as identified by the preceding state p, selected.

In practical terms, if this algorithm is implemented in a computer, each of the m states i has associated with it a minimum distance d_i and a path $\mathbf{c}_i$ nearest to $\mathbf{r}$. In advancing from moment n to $(n+1)$, $\mathbf{c}_i$ not only must be extended but usually requires a transfer from $\mathbf{c}_p$:

$$\mathbf{c}_{i,(n+1)} = (\mathbf{c}_{p,n}, \mathbf{c}_{p,n} \rightarrow \mathbf{c}_{i,n+1})$$

In short, the software must transfer a list of states, corresponding to a codevector, from one state p and attach it (extended) to state i. This requirement to maintain m extending lists and to transfer them between states is not complicated, but it is messy to handle and makes for relatively slow execution of the algorithm, particularly when it is remembered that there are also jm comparisons to make in the minimisation procedure, if there are j possible input paths to each state.

As discussed. the algorithm maintains m "nearest" codevector paths, but when decoding we only want *one*, the overall nearest. This is achieved first by noting that the effect of a few symbol errors, causing $\mathbf{r}$ to deviate from the codevector transmitted, wears off as n increases. For a while, several states and their associated nearest paths may appear equally good, but eventually the algorithm is going to settle down and the diverging contenders for the overall optimum will converge again. There will be *one* optimum path prior to this convergence point, and subsequent to it the paths must spread out to reach the m states we are considering. Thus, after a certain time, t, all the m paths $\mathbf{c}_{i,n}$ at time n will be identical from time instant $(n-t)$ backward. These states can be saved as the decoded codevector, and the m running codevectors can be truncated at this point, so that each has length vt. (The saved states prior to time $(n-t)$ are readily converted into the input symbol stream if the encoding procedure is known.)

Second, although the most recent portion of length vt of the m contending codevectors can easily be selected on the basis of overall nearness to $\mathbf{r}$, this would be a mistake. It is the nature of the encoding process that being in state i at instant n affects the subsequent states attainable and the symbols emitted. Not to observe those symbols and include them in the decision as to which state we are in (i.e., which is the overall nearest path) is to negate the whole purpose of the code. Accordingly, the usual process of bringing decoding to an end is for the encoder to *enforce* convergence on a predetermined state by appending a fixed sequence of input symbols (e.g., all zeros) to the preceding arbitrary data symbols.

The decoder then picks the path associated with this predetermined state as the overall nearest, when transmission ceases. Alternatively, the encoder can simply insert (bt) arbitrary symbols after the end of the input data and let the decoder make no choice with regard to the last vt received.

In practice, because trellis codes consist of a stream of blocks, there are often synchronisation problems. Where does the stream begin? Where does it end? Given that v symbols are emitted at a time, as a block, the first requirement is that the decoder at least aligns itself with the block boundary. With Viterbi decoding this is achieved by noting the distances between the m nearest paths $\mathbf{c}_i$ and the received vector $\mathbf{r}$. If all the distances are similar, alignment has not been achieved, and the decoder should shift one symbol position and try again. When correct alignment has been achieved, the decoder can search for a known *preamble*, a fixed pattern of input symbols transmitted before the data, and synchronise itself with that. All this takes time, and preambles may be many hundreds of bits in length.

The end of the stream may be determined by information contained in the data (e.g., a count of symbols included at the start), by convention (e.g., all streams are of a certain length), or by an explicit postamble, or pattern of symbols used to denote the end. In this last case there are clearly transparency problems, that is, the data are not allowed to contain the terminating pattern.

5.2 LINEAR CONVOLUTIONAL CODES

Trellis codes can be generated by using the arrangement in Figure 5.2. Symbols (e.g., bits) are shifted as input into the register, b at a time. The register holds kb symbols, where k is the constraint length. v combinatorial circuits are fed from the kb stages of the register, each circuit producing a single symbol output. The total of v outputs is sampled one after the other each time interval, to give v outputs for b inputs and a coderate b/v.

If the combinatorial circuits consist of modulo-2 additon (XOR) of a selection of register stages (the other stages being omitted), then the trellis code becomes a *convolutional code*. It is *linear* in the sense that if x_1 and x_2 are two input sequences giving output codevectors y_1 and y_2, respectively, then the input sequence $(x_1 + x_2)$ gives output $(y_1 + y_2)$, where $+$ means XOR. $y = 0$, the all-zero output stream, is a codevector.

The distances between codevectors can be considered by looking at the weights of codevectors, because the difference of two codevectors is a codevector. If one of the combinatorial circuits is fed from a single stage only in the register (usually the first one, for decoding convenience), the convolutional code generated is systematic.

For an example, consider Figure 5.3, which shows the generating circuit for a $1/2$-rate systematic convolutional code, with $b = 1$, $v = 2$, $k = 3$. The state of the generator is determined by the leftmost $k - 1 = 2$ bits, so that when a new $(b = 1)$ input bit enters, it and the state (shifted) determine the output.

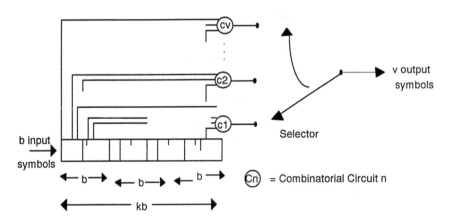

Figure 5.2 Generation of a trellis code with a shift register.

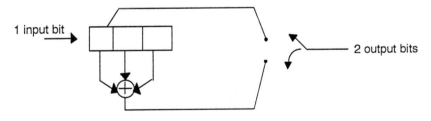

Figure 5.3 Generating a $\frac{1}{2}$-rate convolutional code.

This can be represented in a state diagram, Figure 5.4, which shows the transitions with the input bit causing the transition at the start of each arrow, and the two output bits emitted at the head. Obviously we can also illustrate the encoder as a trellis, as in Figure 5.5.

Labelling the states $00 = a$, $10 = b$, $11 = c$, $01 = d$ and starting in state $00 = a$, we can tabulate the response to various input sequences, as shown in Table 5.1.

Table 5.1 indicates that we should be careful when talking about the distance of a convolutional code. The constraint length $k(= 3$ in this case) determines the interdependence of output symbols, and it is perhaps tempting to state that when

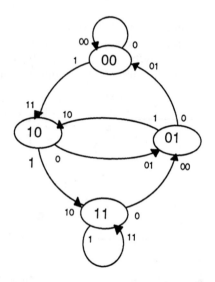

Figure 5.4 State diagram for code of Figure 5.3.

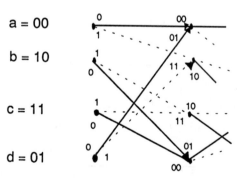

Figure 5.5 Trellis for code of Figure 5.3.

considering decoding techniques it is sufficient to make comparisons between received and codevectors using kv symbols; for example, take t, the interval back in time mentioned in the Viterbi algorithm, as $t = k$. The example shows that if we did that, then the $d = 4$ code would effectively have distance $d = 3$, because the codevector generated by input 1100 is 111000 if we confine ourselves to considering only $kv = 6$ bits.

Put another way, two consecutive error bits, $\dots 0011000000.$, added to the all-zero codevector would logically result in erroneous decoding to a restored input sequence $..0110...$ as opposed to being flagged as uncorrectable because equidistant from 0011010100 and 0011100001. Generally, by *distance* is meant the *free distance*, which is the minimum distance over all codevectors between any pair that start with differing bits considering arbitrary many bits in the sequence.

The depth of decoding, the number of consecutive bits taken into the decision-making process, should be at least kv, and as we have seen usually more , so that the distance used in decoding is the free distance.

We can also represent the behaviour of a convolutional code analytically as follows.

$$y_{s,i} = \sum_{j=0,(k-1)} g_{s,j} x_{i-j} \qquad 1 \leq s \leq v \qquad (5.1)$$

Here s identifies a bit in the output block of v bits; $g_{s,j}$ corresponds to the connections in the XOR combinatorial circuit corresponding to s; and y is the output, x the input sequence.

If we define

$$x(T) = x_0 + Tx_1 + T^2x_2 + T^3x_3\dots$$

$$y(T) = y_0 + Ty_1 + T^2y_2 + T^3y_3\dots$$

Table 5.1

Input	State Sequence	Output
100	abda	110101
1100	abcda	11100001
10100	abdbda	1101100101
110100	abcdbda	111000100101
11100	abccda	1110110001
⋮	⋮	⋮

where T is a *delay operator*, then we have

$$y_s(T) = g_s(T)x(T) \tag{5.2}$$

with

$$g_s(T) = g_{s,0} + g_{s,1} T + g_{s,2} T^2 + \cdots + g_{s,k-1} T^{k-1}$$

as can be seen by collecting together the coefficients of a given power of T and using equation (5.1). Equations (5.1) and (5.2) define $y(\ )$ as the convolution of $x(\ )$ with respect to $g(\ )$ and hence justify the use of the term *convolutional codes*.

In the example of Figure 5.3 the generating functions are given by

$$g_1(T) = 1$$

$$g_2(T) = 1 + T + T^2$$

and if, for example,

$$x(T) = 0 + T^3 + T^4 + 0$$

then

$$y_1(T) = T^3 + T^4$$

$$y_2(T) = T^3 + T^6$$

so that the output from sampling y_1 and y_2 alternately is ..001110000100.... .

Before beginning a more detailed analysis of convolutional codes, it is worth asking the question: Have we any criteria for "good" codes, and how do we find such codes? Clearly we would like the distance of the code to be as large as possible. Remembering that for linear block codes the maximum distance is $(n - k + 1)$, where $(n - k)$ is the number of check digits, it is remarkable that even in our simple example with each block having only 2 bits (1 data, 1 a check bit) the minimum distance is 4. This has been achieved by pushing out the check bits over the constraint length.

Longer constraint lengths are necessary for, but do not always give, greater distances. On the other hand, long constraint lengths give rise to heavy computation if, for example, the Viterbi decoding algorithm is used. A shorter constraint length may be feasible if we have more check bits to provide the distance. But this will then imply a lower code rate as v increases and b/v decreases. As always, compromises between distance, coderate, and complexity (as represented by the constraint length) are necessary.

As for *finding* a good code, assuming we are agreed on the criteria for what is good, it is often easiest to use a computer search through all codes, subject to certain constraints, using various analytical techniques to determine their properties for comparison.

5.2.1 Control of Decoding Errors

One of the important constraints that must be observed in choosing arbitrary codes for analysis is to avoid those that can cause infinite decoding errors. This could occur if a source vector of infinite weight can be encoded into a codevector of finite weight. If this is so, an error pattern of finite weight could be mapped into the codevector in question as being the nearest and could then be decoded into an infinite weight source vector, that is, an infinite decoding error.

Using (5.2), if the infinite polynomial $x_0(T)$ gives rise to a finite polynomial $y_{s,0}(T)$; then an error pattern on transmission $e_s(T) = y_{s,0}(T)$ will give rise to an infinite error on decoding given by

$$e_s(T)/g_s(T)$$

For this problem to occur, all $y_s(T), s = 1$ to v, must be finite for some infinite $x(T)$. This will happen if the $g_s(T)$ have a common factor $h(T)$ (not equal to T^m for some m), because in this case all $y_s(T) = g_s(T)x(T)$ will be finite when $x(T)$ is infinite and equal to $1/h(T)$. For example, if $g_1(T) = 1 + T, g_2(T) = 1 + T^2$ (see Figure 5.6), then $x(T) = 1/(1 + T) = 1 + T + T^2 + T^3 + \dots$ will give $y_1(T) = 1$, $y_2(T) = 1 + T$.

Conversely a 3-bit error corresponding to these values of y_1 and y_2 would be decoded to an infinite series of 1's for addition to the correct vector, complementing it completely. $11010000\dots$ would be decoded to $111111\dots$, not $00000\dots$. It is

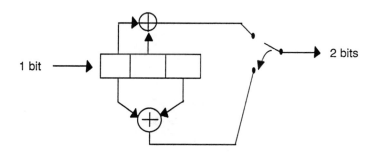

Figure 5.6 A bad code giving infinite errors.

clear that *if* the *code is systematic* no such $h(T)$ can exist, and the problem does not arise.

5.3 ANALYSIS OF CONVOLUTIONAL CODES

If good convolutional codes are to be found by inspection rather than by construction, it is important to be able to analyse a code's properties, and in particular its weight distribution. This can be done readily with a technique first described by Viterbi [13] by considering the state diagram and to that end Figure 5.7, which is simply Figure 5.4 "opened" at the 00 state, will serve as an example.

The basic codevector may be taken as all zeros, and other codevectors are found by leaving state 00 at x, wandering round the state diagram, and returning eventually to state 00 at y. The nature of these excursions can be analysed with the equations

$$b = LND^2x + LND\, d$$
$$c = LND^2c + LND\, b$$
$$d = Lc + LDb$$
$$y = LDd$$

$$(5.3)$$

In (5.3) D is a distance operator, whose exponent signifies the distance between the symbols emitted on the transition and the all-zero emission (that would occur if we remained at 00), that is, the weight of the codevector. Thus, state b can be reached by two transitions: one from x with distance 2, one from d with distance 1. State c can be reached from c or b; state d from c or b; state y from d. The

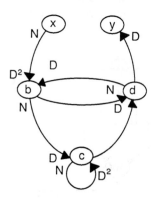

Figure 5.7 The state diagram of Figure 5.3.

exponent of the operator L gives the length of the transition in interstate hops and is always 1 in (5.3). The exponent of the operator N gives the number of *input* 1's required to make the transition; 0 or 1 in (5.3).

We can "solve" (5.3) for y in terms of x, and the result will give us all the possible excursions from x to y with their distances (D's exponent), length (L's exponent), and number of input 1's (N's exponent). With some algebraic manipulation we find

$$y = xL^3ND^4(1 + LN - LND^2)/(1 - (LN + L^2N + L^3N^2)D^2 + L^3N^2D^4)$$
$$= x[D^4L^3N(1 + LN) + D^6L^5N^2(1 + N + 2LN + L^2N^2) + D^8(\ )...]$$

(5.4)

Equation (5.4) states that there are two codevectors of weight 4 (corresponding to D^4), one of length 3 generated by a single input 1, one of length 4 generated by two input 1's. It also states that there are *five* codevectors of weight 6 (D^6), two of length 5, two of length 6, one of length 7, and so on.

The vectors are given by the following paths:

xbdy	D^4L^3N
xbcdy	$D^4L^4N^2$
xbdbdy	$D^6L^5N^2$
xbccdy	$D^6L^5N^3$
xbcdbdy	$D^6L^6N^3$
xbdbcdy	$D^6L^6N^3$
xbcdbcdy	$D^6L^7N^4$

Thus, (5.4) gives the weight structure of the code and also indicates how it arises by means of the L and N operators. This in turn can be used to put bounds on the probability of incorrect decoding.

In this general case, in place of equation (5.4) we have

$$y = F(L, N, D)$$
$$= \sum_k f_k(L, N)D^k$$

(5.5)

The expression $f_k(L, N)$ evaluated with $L = 1, N = 1$, that is, $f_k(1, 1)$ is simply the number of codevectors of weight k.

Equation (5.5) can be used to establish bounds on the probability of erroneous decoding. Consider a sequence of bit errors that causes the recipient to believe that a codevector different to the one really transmitted was intended. This would occur if the error pattern is nearer to a codevector with weight not equal to zero than to the zero codevector. If P_k is the probability of an error pattern nearer to a codevector of weight k than to the zero codevector occurring, then

$$E_i \le \sum_k f_k(1,1)P_k \tag{5.6}$$

where E_i is the probability of a wrong decoding decision being arrived at in respect of this error sequence starting at bit i. Inequality (5.6) is an inequality, not an equation, because the P_k are not necessarily disjoint and an error pattern could be nearer to two or more nonzero codevectors than to zero, so it would be counted two or more times in (5.6).

Over n received bits, the probability of a decoding error is then bounded by (nE_i). Again this is an upper bound because these n error sequences are distinct only if they have returned to y from x in Figure 5.7 before setting out again; this is determined by the exponent of L in (5.5) (and the minimum value for this is usually considerably greater than 1). Note that (5.6) presupposes that the decoding technique picks the nearest codevector to the received vector, considering *all* codevectors. Such a technique is the Viterbi algorithm, but other techniques may not perform a complete search of the codespace, and (5.6) need not necessarily hold.

For given codes and given assumptions about the occurrences of errors (e.g., the binary symmetric channel, BSC), it is possible to put an upper bound, if not an explicit value, on P_k. For example, Viterbi gives

$$P_k < \left(2(p(1-p))^{1/2}\right)^k$$

for the BSC. In our example we would then find from (5.4) that

$$E_i \le 2\left(2(p(1-p))^{1/2}\right)^4 + 5\left(2(p(1-p))^{1/2}\right)^6 + \dots$$

$$= 32\,p^2(1-p)^2 + 320\,p^3(1-p)^3 + \dots$$

For $p = 10^{-3}$ $\qquad E_i < 4 \times 10^{-5}$

$\qquad p = 10^{-4}$ $\qquad E_i < 4 \times 10^{-7}$ very approximately.

Equation (5.5) can also be used to find a bound on the *postdecoding* bit error rate. If we set

$$g_k(1,\mathrm{N}) = \partial(f_k(1,\mathrm{N}))/\partial\mathrm{N}$$

then

$$\sum_k g_k(1,1)P_k \tag{5.7}$$

gives the number of *decoded* bits in error corresponding to each erroneously selected codevector of weight k, multiplied by a bound on the probability of this occurring as a weighting factor. In short (5.7) is a bound on the expectation value for *postdecoding* errors. In our example this is

$$3P_4 + 15P_6 + \ldots$$

giving an expected postdecoding bit error rate for the BSC of $< 5 \times 10^{-5}$ (when $p = 10^{-3}$) or $< 5 \times 10^{-7}$ (when $p = 10^{-4}$).

5.4 ERROR CORRECTING WITH CONVOLUTIONAL CODES

Decoding convolutional codes, that is, correcting the errors occurring in transit to obtain the originally transmitted codevector, can be performed (as we have seen) using the Viterbi algorithm. The algorithm is optimum, in the sense that the nearest codevector to the received vector is found, the entire space of codevectors being searched. The algorithm does, however, become quite slow and cumbersome as the constraint length k increases and it becomes necessary to manage $2^{b(k-1)}$ states assuming the input is binary. Popular codes such as the $b = 1$, $k = 7$ code with

$$g_1(T) = 1 + T + T^2 + T^3 + T^6$$

$$g_2(T) = 1 + T^2 + T^3 + T^5 + T^6$$

and weight equal to 10 correspond, in many cases, to the maximum computing load the system can reasonably support using the Viterbi technique; if larger distances are required, other approaches to decoding must be employed. This section considers some examples of such techniques, but first we give a concrete example of Viterbi decoding applied to the code we have already analysed and whose generator is shown in Figure 5.3.

The decoding process is illustrated in trellis form in Figure 5.8. The transmitted codevector, corresponding to the state sequence *abccdbdaabcda*, is

$$1110110010010010011100001$$

There are assumed to be two errors, and the received vector is

$$1110110110011110011100001$$

In Figure 5.8, at each transition the distance between the pair of bits in the

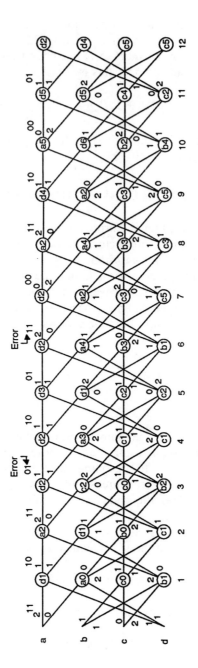

Figure 5.8 Viterbi decoding example.

received vector and the pair that should be transmitted for that transition, the *metric*, is shown on the transition arrow. At each time interval, for each of the four states, the accummulated minimum metric for that state, and the preceding state on the path that gives rise to that metric, is shown. Thus, state *d*, after the first time interval, can be reached from *b*, (metric = 1 since 11 was received and the proper emission is 01) or from *c*(metric = 2 since 11 was received and the proper emission is 00); therefore state *d* is labelled with *b* as the preceding state on the optimum path, with an accummulated metric $0 + 1 = 1$.

In the fourth time interval an error is processed, and both states *c* and *d* have equally good accummulated metrics; but after the fifth interval state *b* is unique in having metric = 1. The path can be traced back using the indicated preceding states to give the correct sequence (in reverse order) *bdccba*. In the seventh interval another error occurs, and the algorithm again handles this correctly, reducing the two optimum paths at time 7 to one, with metric = 2, at time 8. It should be pointed out that although the distance of the code is only 4 we have successfully decoded two errors; this is because the error pattern, which is...0100001000...is nearer to the all-zero codevector than to the weight = 4 vectors...11010100...and...11100001.... However, if the error were ..01000001.. we can see from Figure 5.9 (which picks up Figure 5.8 at time 6) that by time 9 we have incorrectly established the optimum path with metric = 2 as reaching state *b*; with a path history (in reverse order) *baaadcccba* or (in forward order) a state sequence *abcccdaaab* with emitted vector 111011110001000011, which is nearer to the received vector 111011011001000011 than it is to the real transmitted vector 111011001001010011.

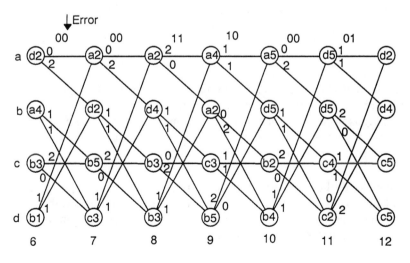

Figure 5.9 Viterbi decoding with a different error.

5.4.1 Soft-Decision Decoding

The Viterbi algorithm can be readily adapted to "soft-decision" decoding (see Section 1.1). In this case it would be more normal to work with a metric that required maximisation, rather than the "hard-decision" metric of the Hamming distance, which requires minimisation. For example, the received binary symbol 0 or 1 might be accompanied by a reliability or probability factor ($\geq 1/2$) and the metric to the *same symbol* in a codevector being matched to the received vector would then be (a function of) that factor, while the metric to the *complementary symbol* would be (a function of) unity minus that factor. In Section 1.1 this approach was illustrated, starting with the assumption that the reliability factors were provided bit by bit by receiving equipment, such as a demodulator of analogue waveforms. Another view could be that the input to the decoder is taken to be "hard" 0's and 1's from the receiving equipment, to which we attach standard probability factors, $(1 - p)$ for the same symbol, p for the complementary symbol, assuming the model of the binary symmetric channel. The metric used would then be

$$\log_2\left((1-p)/\tfrac{1}{2}\right) = 1 + \log_2(1-p) \quad \text{between the same symbols}$$

$$\log_2\left(p/\tfrac{1}{2}\right) = 1 + \log_2(p) \quad \text{between complementary symbols} \qquad (5.8)$$

where the factor $1/2$ is a normaliser. The rationale is that if the y is the received bit and x the transmitted bit

$$\text{Prob}(y = 0) = \text{Prob}(y = 0|x = 0) \quad \text{Prob}(x = 0) + \text{Prob}(y = 0|x = 1)\text{Prob}(x = 1)$$

$$= (1 - p)/2 + p/2$$

$$= 1/2$$

and similarly $\text{Prob}(y = 1) = 1/2$, assuming $x = 0$ or 1 with equal probability, so that the arguments of the logarithms are $\text{Prob}(y|x)/\text{Prob}(y)$.

The reason for using logarithms is to make the metric *additive* rather than multiplicative and is based on the concept of maximising the likelihood of the chosen path through trellis:

(likelihood of optimum path to state $n_{(t+1)}$ at time $(t + 1)$) =
(likelihood of optimum path to state n_t at time t) multiplied by
(probability that the symbols emitted were those of transition n_t to $n_{(t+1)}$ given the actual symbols received)

Taking logarithms to base 2, we maximise the log-likelihood, and obtain from the last term the additive metric $(1 + \log_2(1 - p))$ or $(1 + \log_2 p)$. Given that the rate at which symbols are complemented by errors is p, we can say that the expected metric of the correct path over N bits received is

$$N(p(1 + \log_2 p) + (1 - p)(1 + \log_2(1 - p)))$$
$$= N(1 - H(p)) \tag{5.9}$$

where $H(\ )$ is the entropy function.

If, on the other hand, we consider an incorrect path through the trellis, and supposing that the probability that the received symbols and the symbols emitted according to the path agree is $1/2$ (i.e., random), then the expected metric for an incorrect path is

$$N(\tfrac{1}{2}(1 + \log_2 p) + \tfrac{1}{2}(1 + \log_2(1 - p)))$$
$$= N(1 + (\log_2 p + \log_2(1 - p))/2) \tag{5.10}$$

For $p < 1/2$, the metric for the correct path (5.9) is positive and increases with N. The metric for an incorrect path (5.10) is negative and decreases with N.

Although the use of soft decision with bit-by-bit reliability factors covering a range of values (if they are available) can significantly improve the performance of the algorithm, the two-valued scheme for the metric of (5.8) is of little value with the Viterbi technique. The use of the normal Hamming distance for the metric is sufficient if the Viterbi decoder receives unqualified 0's and 1's; the metric of (5.8) is more appropriate to decoding techniques that are based on the metric's rate of change, as given by (5.9) and (5.10), than on its absolute value.

5.4.2 Sequential Decoding

Such a technique is that of *sequential decoding*. The general idea behind this technique is to follow the transmitted codevector through the state diagram (or equivalently the tree or trellis), making instant decisions as to the path as each v new received symbols are processed. The new node on the path is that which can be reached from the previous node and which maximises the accummulated metric. This process continues with the metric increasing until an incorrect branch is taken and as a consequence the metric starts to decrease. When this occurs, an appropriate algorithm is invoked which backtracks along the path and tries forward moves along branches that were previously rejected as not being optimum, until a new path with an increasing metric is again established.

When a metric such as that of (5.8) is used (and sometimes a biasing constant is also added to it), there is a sharp negative turn in the accummulated value when an incorrect path is chosen. The extent of this is controllable, to a certain extent, by choosing the number of connection points in the polynomials $g_s(T)$, that is, the nonzero coefficients. A single wrong input bit will clearly complement the output bit y_s each time it is shifted into a stage in the shift register corresponding to such a connection. Thus, the $g_s(T)$ can be chosen not only to maximise distance but also to affect the sensitivity of the algorithm used.

The most commonly used form of sequential decoding algorithm is due to Fano [14]. It relies on a threshold value that is raised in fixed increments as the metric increases. Very roughly the algorithm proceeds as follows:

1. Calculate the new accummulated metric by adding in the new (maximum value) metric corresponding to the latest received v bits and the newly chosen node.
2. If the new accummulated metric exceeds the current threshold by the value of the increment or more, increment the threshold and repeat the procedure for the next v received bits by returning to step 1. If the metric simply exceeds the current threshold, also return to step 1 without any incrementation. Otherwise, go to step 3.
3. The metric is decreasing, so backtrack one node and try an alternative branch from it that gives a metric above the threshold; if no such branch exists, go back a further node and try again, and so on. If branches are found that allow us to advance successfully again to include the most recent v received bits, with the accummulated metric still above the threshold, we have established a new acceptable path. Return to step 1 and continue. Otherwise, go to step 4.
4. Decrement the threshold, return to the original node considered before backtracking began, and try to advance with this new lower threshold. Return to step 2.

During implementation of this algorithm care must be taken not to get stuck in a loop by raising the threshold again, until a new successful path is firmly established. The advantage of sequential decoding is that it can be used with codes having long constraint lengths (to allow large distances) where Viterbi decoding is impracticable. Also, if there are not too many errors, it is much faster than the Viterbi method, because an exhaustive search for the correct path, involving backtracking, is rarely undertaken.

5.4.3 Feedback Decoding

Another method for correcting errors in convolutional codes is called *feedback decoding*. The approach is to accummulate several sets of received symbols (or of quantities derived from them) at the decoder before making a decoding decision on the oldest. When the decision is made, an estimate of the corresponding data symbol(s) is passed to the application. If the value decided on implies a change in any subsequent received symbols still waiting to be processed, this change is fed back and applied to those symbols. The effect of this procedure is that once a firm decision has been taken and its consequences have been executed, decoding proceeds only within a limited set of branches of the code tree. Feedback decoding is thus suboptimum, in that the entire code space is not searched, as in Viterbi decoding or sequential decoding with unlimited backtracking.

More precisely we can say that at instant n we have received $y_{(nv+1)}$ to $y_{(n+1)v}$ and if the "decoding depth" is L, the process involves making a firm decision on the data $x_{((n-L)b+1)}$ to $x_{(n-L+1)b}$, which were putatively input to the encoder.

The basis of the decision is that those $x_{((n-L)b+1)}$ to $x_{(n-L+1)b}$ are chosen that give rise to a path through the state diagram that begins at the previously chosen $x_{((n-L-1)b+1)}$ to $x_{(n-L)b}$ and that gives rise to emitted symbols nearest to the actual $(L+1)v$ received symbols $y_{((n-L)v+1)}$ to $y_{(n+1)v}$. It is obvious that L should at least equal $(k-1)$, where k is the constraint length; the remarks in Section 5.2 indicate that usually it should be greater.

An example of one form of feedback decoding is *syndrome feedback*, which is a technique applicable only to systematic convolutional codes. It is illustrated in Figure 5.10 for a code with $b = 1$, for simplicity. The received message or data bit m'_{n+1} (the dash signifies that m'_{n+1} is a possibly corrupted version of the transmitted m_{n+1}) is put through the code generator to regenerate the associated check or parity bits $p''_{i,n+1}$ for $i = 1$ to v. These are subtracted from the received parity bits $p'_{i,n+1}$ to give syndromes $S_{i,n+1}$.

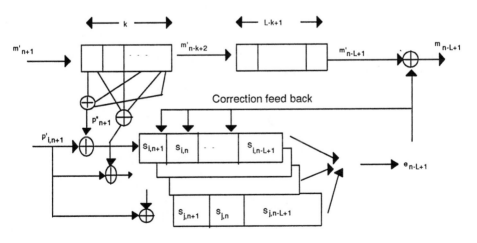

Figure 5.10 Syndrome feedback decoding.

The syndromes are accummulated, and the decoding decision for m_{n-L+1} is made on the basis of syndromes $S_{i,n-L+1}$ to $S_{i,n+1}$ for $i = 1$ to v, where L is the decoding depth. As shown below, the syndromes depend only on the transmission errors, so that the output of the decision-making process is in fact e_{n-L+1}, an error bit equal to 0 or 1, which is subtracted (XOR) from m'_{n-L+1} to give m_{n-L+1}. It is interesting to compare this procedure with syndrome decoding for linear block codes (see Chapter 2). In such codes we have the generator matrix $\mathbf{G}$ and the null matrix $\mathbf{H}$ given by

$$\mathbf{G} = (\mathbf{I}, \mathbf{P}) \quad \text{and} \quad \mathbf{H} = (-\mathbf{P}^T, \mathbf{I})$$

where $\mathbf{P}$ is the k by $(n - k)$ parity matrix.

A codevector $\mathbf{c} = \mathbf{mG} = (\mathbf{m}, \mathbf{p})$, where p is an $(n - k)$ vector representing the check or parity digits. If $\mathbf{c}' = (\mathbf{m}', \mathbf{p}')$ is received, we calculate the syndrome

$$\mathbf{s} = \mathbf{c}'\mathbf{H}^T = -\mathbf{m}'\mathbf{p} + \mathbf{p}'$$
$$= \mathbf{p}' - \mathbf{p}''$$

where $\mathbf{p}''$ is the $(n - k)$ parity vector recalculated from the received $\mathbf{m}'$.
But

$$\mathbf{p}' - \mathbf{p}'' = \mathbf{p} + \mathbf{e}_p - (\mathbf{p} + \mathbf{e}_m\mathbf{P})$$
$$= \mathbf{e}_p - \mathbf{e}_m\mathbf{P}$$

where $\mathbf{e}_p$ and $\mathbf{e}_m$ are the error vectors added to p and m, respectively. Thus,

$$\mathbf{s} = \mathbf{e}_p - \mathbf{e}_m\mathbf{P} \tag{5.11}$$

So the syndrome of systematic block codes is independent of the codeword sent and depends only on the errors.

For syndrome decoding of convolutional codes we have

$$S_n = p'_n - \sum_j g_j m'_{(n-j)}$$

$$= -\sum_j g_j(m_{n-j} + e_{m,(n-j)}) + p_n + e_{p,n}$$

So

$$S_n = e_{p,n} - \sum_j g_j e_{m,(n-j)} \tag{5.12}$$

Equation (5.12) is directly analogous to (5.11). In (5.12) the g_j are the coefficients of $g(T)$, (see [5.1]), and we have considered only one syndrome (equivalent to the case $v = 1$) to simplify the notation.

From (5.12) we see that the syndromes of systematic convolutional codes depend only on the *errors* in the parity check bits (e_p) and the message data bits (e_m), not on the message itself.

For an example, consider the code generated in Figure 5.3.

5.4.4 Syndrome Decoding: A Worked Example

The syndrome decoder for the code of Figure 5.3 is illustrated in Figure 5.11, with a decoding depth $L = k - 1 = 2$. There are thus three registers for holding syndromes, labelled S_{n+1}, S_n, S_{n-1}, where S_{n-1} is the oldest. The output from the decision-making process, whose inputs are the syndromes, is the message error bit $e_{m,n-1}$. It is used first to complement the corresponding message bit m'_{n-1}; and second to complement S_{n+1} and S_n, since an error in m'_{n-1} will have affected them as well as S_{n-1}.

The decision-making process is performed using the look-up Table 5.2. There are eight possible states for S_{n+1}, S_n and S_{n-1}, and for each state a decision on $e_{m,n-1}$ must be made, 0 or 1. The rule used is that if a *single* bit error in message (e_m) or parity check bit (e_p) could give rise to the state in question, it is assumed to have done so. If that bit error was $e_{m,n-1}$, then 1 is output; otherwise, 0. This look-up table shows the presumed errors giving rise to the state, and the consequent output $e_{m,n-1}$. In two cases $(S_{n+1}, S_n, S_{n-1} = 011)$ and $(S_{n+1}, S_n, S_{n-1} = 101)$ no single error could have given rise to the states, but three versions of double errors could have done so.

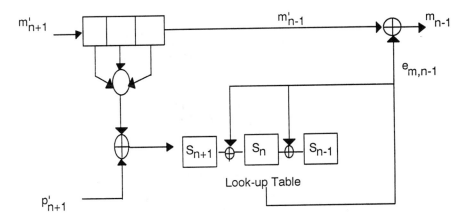

Figure 5.11 Syndrome feedback decoder for code of Figure 5.3.

The value for $e_{m,n-1}$ which occurs most frequently in those three versions is chosen. (Remember that the code has weight equal to 4, and cannot (in general) correct double errors.)

As an example, consider the received sequence 00101001 where the first message bit is on the right (the second bit being a parity bit). It will give rise to the following syndromes and outputs

Syndromes	Decison $(e_{m,n-1})$	Output (m_{n-1})
100	0	0
010	0	0
001	0	1
000	0	0

which implies that the transmitted vector was 00101011 (reading from the right), being that generated by a single nonzero bit in the message.

For a second example, we take as received vector (reading from the right) 00101111, which gives rise to

Syndromes	Decision $(e_{m,n-1})$	Output (m_{n-1})
000	0	0
100	0	0
110	0	1
111	1	0
000	0	0

In the fourth step the output $e_{m,n-1}$ cancels the (erroneous) third bit received

Table 5.2

S_{n+1}	S_n	S_{n-1}	Most likely errors	Decision
0	0	0	None	$e_{m,n-1} = 0$
0	0	1	$e_{p,n-1} = 1$	$e_{m,n-1} = 0$
0	1	0	$e_{p,n} = 1$	$e_{m,n-1} = 0$
0	1	1	$e_{m,n-1} = 1$ and $e_{p,n+1} = 1$ or $e_{m,n-1} = 1$ and $e_{m,n+1} = 1$ or $e_{p,n-1} = 1$ and $e_{p,n} = 1$	$e_{m,n-1} = 1$
1	0	0	$e_{p,n+1} = 1$	$e_{m,n-1} = 0$
1	0	1	$e_{m,n-1} = 1$ and $e_{p,n} = 1$ or $e_{m,n+1} = 1$ and $e_{p,n-1} = 1$ or $e_{p,n+1} = 1$ and $e_{p,n-1} = 1$	$e_{m,n-1} = 0$
1	1	0	$e_{m,n} = 1$	$e_{m,n-1} = 0$
1	1	1	$e_{m,n-1} = 1$	$e_{m,n-1} = 1$

(second message bit) to give the correct value for the message bit; and the feedback complements S_{n+1} and S_n so that the syndromes are zero for the fifth step.

It will be noted that the decoding depth $L = k - 1$, which is the minimum advisable; and that it was pointed out that larger values of L are desirable because over kv symbols the distance could be less than the free distance. (In the case of this code, over six symbols we can have distance = 3 as given by the vector 11100001, reading left to right.) However, if we work with S_{n+1}, S_n, S_{n-1}, and S_{n-2} and a 16-state look-up table we find that there is no improvement in the decision-making process. This is partly due to the fact that the code's distance is 4, so that double-errors are always going to give rise to ambiguities. It is also due to the nature of syndrome decoding, which works with a combination (XOR) of message and parity bits, rather than the individual bits, and as such inherently has a coarser view of discrepancies and inconsistencies.

5.5 BLOCK CODES AND CONVOLUTIONAL CODES

We conclude this chapter with some brief remarks contrasting block and convolutional codes.

Block codes, as we have seen in Chapters 2, 3, and 4, are built on mathematical concepts such as vector spaces over a finite field for general linear codes or, in the case of cyclic codes, ideals in a ring of polynomials.

This mathematical foundation permits not only a reasonably thorough analysis of a code's properties, it also allows codes to be *constructed* with predetermined properties, using techniques such as that of "consecutive roots" for cyclic codes.

In the case of convolutional codes the mathematical basis is much weaker. Certain techniques are available for analysing a given code (e.g., using the operators D, N and L), but the construction of convolutional codes is more a matter of trial and error than anything else.

When it comes to decoding, the same general situation applies. Block codes are decoded using relatively sophisticated mathematics, with computations in finite fields, Newton's identities, and so on. Convolutional codes are decoded with heuristic algorithms designed essentially to search the codespace, with some possible restrictions in the name of efficiency.

With regard to the properties of the codes we have seen already that linearity imposes a severe constraint on block codes. Adding another bit of length (doubling the number of vectors in the total space) *at most* doubles the number of codewords in the subspace. Similarly, for an (n, k) code there are $(n - k)$ check digits, and the maximum distance of the code d is bound by

$$d \leq n - k + 1$$

a value attained only with Reed-Solomon codes. If the coderate $r = k/n$ is fixed, then d/n has a fixed upper bound $(1 - r + 1/n)$. In fact the Plotkin bound (Chapter 2) shows that d/n has a more severe upper limit, namely, $(1 - r)/2$. In the case of cyclic codes, if m is the degree of the minimal polynomial of the basic root, we have (very approximately) $md/2 < (n - k)$, since the number of polynomial factors required to produce a distance d, with d consecutive roots, is $d/2$. Therefore $d/n < 2(1 - r)/m$. But $m = \log_2 n$ approximately; so that as n increases, keeping the coderate constant, d/n *decreases* in general. The block codes we have looked at are severely constrained as to their distance, not in absolute terms but in proportion to the code length; and the ratio d/n is the critical parameter when we consider the objective of correcting random bit errors of rate p. We want $d/2 = t > pn$.

The situation with convolutional codes is very different. At first sight they have small distances and low coderates. However, the distance is a local property. It is true that a convolutional code cannot correct more than $(d - 1)/2$ errors if they all occur in a short interval, but if they are scattered over a longer period they are correctable.

If the codevector of least weight d represents a digression from the all-zero path of length L, then (roughly speaking) any number of error bursts of less than $(d - 1)/2$ bits can be corrected, provided they are spaced at intervals greater than L. Although there are digressions longer than L, these tend to have proportionally greater distances, so the statement still holds true. However, more important, the coderate, r, has only a tenuous connection with the distance. *The determining factor for the distance is the constraint length*, to which there is essentially no upper limit except that imposed by the complexity of the associated operations, in particular decoding algorithms.

The overall error-correcting capability of a convolutional code therefore principally depends on the constraint length and on the nature of the convolutional polynomials $g_s(T)$, but it cannot usually be expressed as a simple function of these items, but rather by bounding inequalities on the postdecoding error rate, such as that given by the expression of (5.7).

Finally with regard to the low coderates of convolutional codes as commonly used, this is not an inherent property of such codes but again the result of wishing to avoid excessive complexity. To obtain higher coderates than $r = 1/2$ we require $b > 1$. But there are $2^{b(k-1)}$ states (for a binary code), each one of which has 2^b outgoing connections to other states, and also 2^b incoming ones from other states. Figure 5.12 illustrates an extension of our $b = 1, v = 2, k = 3$ 1/2-rate binary code of Figure 5.3 to a 2/3-rate $b = 2, v = 3, k = 3$ code. An attempt to draw the state diagram of this simple scheme will convince the reader how quickly the complexity of the code grows as b increases above unity. Moreover, the code has a poor distance $= 2$ (consider the input $\ldots 0011000000 \ldots$), which is essentially due to the fact that it is systematic, so there is only one parity bit out of the $v = 3$ output bits

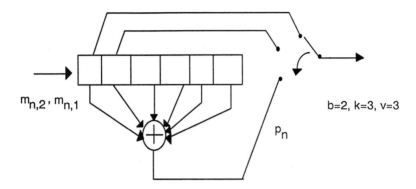

Figure 5.12 A systemate $\frac{2}{3}$-rate code generator.

available for increasing the distance; the other two bits being arbitrary data. In general, the distances of nonsystematic codes, suitably chosen, are greater than those of systematic codes with the same b, v and k, but this improvement is again at the cost of complexity.

The overall conclusion may be put thus:

- Block codes are used when information is naturally structured in blocks; when channel capacity is relatively low and we do not want to waste it further with unnecessarily low coderates; and when quick efficient decoding is required, because of limited processing time available.
- When long streams of relatively unstructured data are transmitted on high-capacity channels (e.g.. satellite 10Mbps channels) and when the complexity of the decoder represents a relatively small proportion of the total cost of receiving equipment (e.g., a satellite receiver), then convolutional codes can offer the best error-correcting solutions.

The interested reader is referred to the many more specialist texts on these topics, for further study [15, 16, 17]. In general, there is no unique solution to any particular error-correcting problem: it is a matter of balancing coderate against code distance; the extent of error correction against the computational complexity; and also taking into account many associated considerations such as synchronisation and the possible use of soft-decision techniques. In many respects the practical application of error-correcting techniques is as much an art as a science.

Appendix A
Information Theory

The relevance of information theory [2] to error-correcting codes is largely confined to two areas:

- Providing an insight into the need for error correction, by analysing redundancy in an information source, and the effect of its removal by compression;
- Providing a measure of information loss on a channel as a result of errors and thus making a link between error rates, channel capacity, and the probability of successful error correction, as in Shannon's Theorem (see Chapter 1).

This appendix looks briefly at both these aspects.

A.1 INFORMATION, ENTROPY, REDUNDANCY AND COMPRESSION

The information associated with an event, E_i, is defined as

$$\text{Info}(i) = \log_2(1/p_i)$$

where p_i is the probability of E_i's occurrence. This information is obtained if E_i occurs. In the absence of E_i's occurrence, it is an "uncertainty", a "lack of information".

The definition satisfies two commonsense requirements.

- The smaller the probability the higher the associated information. If an event is certain (E_i has $p_i = 1$) the occurrence of E_i delivers no information. If p_i is very small, the information delivered is large.
- If E_1 and E_2 are *independent* events, the probability of both occurring is $p_1 p_2$, giving

$$\text{Info}(1, 2) = \log_2(1/p_1 p_2)$$
$$= \log_2(1/p_1) + \log_2(1/p_2)$$
$$= \text{Info}(1) + \text{Info}(2)$$

Thus, the information associated with the joint occurrence of two independent events is the sum of the individual information.

The base 2, for the logarithms, is arbitrary, a scaling factor. If 2, as opposed to some other base, is used, we talk of the information being measured in "bits", *binary information units*. The connection with "ordinary" bits as symbols is obvious, if we consider the probability of a bit being 1 or 0. If this is given by $p = 1/2$, with 1 or 0 equally likely, we have

$$\text{Info} = \log_2(2) = 1 \text{ bit}$$

Thus, one bit symbol holds one information bit.

If a source, S, of information emits one of M symbols at a time, with a probability p_i ($i = 1$ to M) for the ith symbol, we can define the *average information* or *entropy* provided by that source as $H(S)$ with

$$H(S) = \sum_{i=1,M} p_i \log_2(1/p_i) \qquad (A.1)$$

subject to

$$\sum_{i=1,M} p_i = 1$$

Using Lagrange's method of an undetermined multiplier, λ, we can find the maximum value for $H(S)$ by partial differentiation with respect to p_i:

$$\partial\left[H(S) + \lambda\left(\sum p_i - 1\right)\right]\Big/\partial p_i = 0 \qquad (A.2)$$

and solving (A.2) for the p_i.. We get

$$\log_2(1/p_i) - \log_2 e + \lambda = 0$$

which means that all p_i satisfy the same equation and so are equal. Therefore, $p_i = 1/M$

This in turn in (A.1) gives

$$\text{Max}[H(S)] = \log_2 M$$

which is the number of symbol bits required to represent M differing symbols.

The fact that $\log_2 M$ is the *maximum* information suggests that when there is less information from the source it may be possible to represent it with fewer symbol bits. This could be done by using shorter bit strings for the most frequently occurring symbols and longer bit strings for the least frequently occurring symbols, instead of $\log_2 M$ bits for all of them.

We now define the *redundancy* of the source by

$$\text{redundancy} = \log_2 M - H(S)$$

and the percentage redundancy by

$$\text{percentage redundancy} = 100\left[\log_2 M - H(S)\right]/\log_2 M$$

These definitions imply that not only is $H(S)$ the information associated with the source normally less than $\log_2 M$; but that using $\log_2 M$ bits to represent the output of the source is in some sense redundant and unnecessary. This can be put more precisely by stating that using an "immediate" code to represent the M symbols, we can compress the source output so that the *average length* of the symbols, weighted with their probabilities, is (almost) $H(S)$ rather than $\log_2 M$. To see this, we need to prove the theorems that follow, but first we must define an "immediate" code.

An *immediate code* is a representation of a set of symbols (e.g., symbols omitted by a source) that uses a string of symbols selected from a *restricted* alphabet of symbols (e.g., 0 and 1) as codewords, subject to the constraint that no codeword may be equal to or a prefix of any other (where *prefix* means the first few symbols in the representation).

We could represent the source symbols in any way we like as strings in the restricted alphabet. The *immediacy* constraint means that there is no ambiguity in decoding a series of symbols, when no separators are used to break up the series into its component strings of potentially unequal length.

For example, if the four symbols A, B, C, and D are emitted by the source S, and we use a binary alphabet for representation:

- $A = 1, B = 11, C = 110, D = 111$ is *not* immediate
- $A = 1, B = 10, C = 100, D = 1000$ is *not* immediate
- $A = 0, B = 10, C = 110, D = 1110$ *is* immediate

Theorem A.1

For a code over base r (i.e., with r base symbols in its alphabet) and with n_i codewords of length $i, 1 \leq i \leq j, n_j \neq 0$, a necessary and sufficient requirement for it to be *immediate* is

$$r^j \geq n_j + rn_{j-1} + r^2 n_{j-2} + \cdots + r^{j-1} n_1 \tag{A.3}$$

Proof

The inequality is *necessary* because of the prohibition on one codeword being a prefix of any other codeword. Then the n_1 codewords of length 1 "use up" $r^{(j-1)}n_1$ of the possible r^j vectors, because all r^{j-1} values for the $(j-1)$ symbols following the initial symbol are not allowed. Similar reasoning applies to $r^{(j-2)}n_2$, and so on.

But from (A.3) we can deduce a whole series of necessary inequalities by remembering that $n_j \neq 0$. Therefore,

$$r^j > rn_{j-1} + r^2 n_{j-2} + \cdots + r^{j-1} n_1$$

or

$$r^{j-1} > n_{j-1} + rn_{j-2} + \cdots + r^{j-2} n_1$$

Discarding n_{j-1}, n_{j-2}, and so on, successively and dividing by r each time, we get

$$r^{j-1} > n_{j-1} + rn_{j-2} + \cdots + r^{j-2} n_1$$
$$r^{j-2} > n_{j-2} + rn_{j-3} + \cdots + r^{j-3} n_1$$

$$\cdots\cdots\cdots\cdots\cdots\cdots\cdots\cdots\cdots \qquad (A.4)$$

$$r^2 > n_2 + rn_1$$
$$r > n_1$$

The series of inequalities (A.4) are a consequence of (A.3). But given that (A.4) hold, we can *construct* an immediate code by choosing any $n_1(<r)$ symbols for the strings of one symbol in length. This leaves $(r^2 - rn_1) > 0$ strings of length 2 available. Since $n_2 < (r^2 - rn_1)$ we can pick any n_2 of these length -2 strings and leave $r^3 - r(n_2 + rn_1) > 0$ strings of length 3 available from which to pick n_3, and so on.

Therefore, (A.3) is a necessary and sufficient condition for an immediate code.

Theorem A.2

If

$$\sum_{i=1,n} u_i = \sum_{i=1,n} v_i = 1 \quad \text{then}$$

$$\sum_{i=1,n} v_i \log(1/u_i) \geq \sum_{i=1,n} v_i \log(1/v_i) \qquad (A.5)$$

Proof

Consider the inequality $x \geq 1 + \ln x$, where ln is the natural logarithm to base e

Putting $x = u_i/v_i$, we have

$$u_i/v_i \geq 1 + \ln(u_i/v_i)$$

Multiplying by v_i and summing $i = 1$ to n gives

$$\sum_{i=1,n} u_i \geq \sum_{i=1,n} v_i + \sum_{i=1,n} v_i \ln(u_i/v_i)$$

or

$$1 \geq 1 + \sum_{i=1,n} v_i \ln(1/v_i) - \sum_{i=1,n} v_i \ln(1/u_i)$$

so

$$\sum_{i=1,n} v_i \ln(1/u_i) \geq \sum_{i=1,n} v_i \ln(1/v_i)$$

Changing the base of the logarithms merely multiplies this inequality by a positive constant. Therefore, (A.5) holds.

Theorem A.3

The average length, L, of an immediate code is greater than or equal to the entropy of the source measured in bits

$$L \geq H(S)$$

L is defined as

$$L = \sum_{i=1,n} p_i l_i$$

where there are n source symbols to be encoded, and the ith source symbol has probability p_i and is encoded as a string of length l_i in the representational symbols 0 and 1.

Proof

In inequality (A.5) set

$$v_i = p_i \qquad u_i = 2^{-l_i} \Bigg/ \left(\sum_{j=1,n} 2^{-l_j} \right)$$

to give

$$\sum_{i=1,n} p_i l_i + \sum_{i=1,n} p_i \log_2 \left(\sum_{j=1,n} 2^{-l_j} \right) \geq \sum_{i=1,n} p_i \log_2(1/p_i) = H(S)$$

or

$$L \geq H(S) - \log_2 \left(\sum_{i=1,n} 2^{-l_i} \right) \qquad (A.6)$$

But

$$\sum_{i=1,n} 2^{-l_i} = n_1 2^{-1} + n_2 2^{-2} + \cdots + n_j 2^{-j}$$

if there are n_i strings of length l_i, which, using (A.3) of Theorem A.1 with $r = 2$, gives

$$\sum_{i=1,n} 2^{-l_i} \leq 2^j / 2^j = 1 \qquad (A.7)$$

Substituting (A.7) in (A.6) gives

$$L \geq H(S)$$

since

$$\log_2 \left(\sum_{i=1,n} 2^{-l_i} \right) \leq 0$$

Theorem A.3 states, setting $M = n$, that information in the form of source symbols selected from an alphabet of M such symbols, can be compressed by encoding each symbol as a binary string of l_i bits per symbol, but that L has $H(S)$ as a lower bound. Shannon proposed a procedure for performing this encoding that nearly achieves this bound, as follows.

1. List the source symbols S_i in order of decreasing probability p_i.
2. Calculate for each S_i the number of bits l_i to represent it, using the inequalities

$$\log_2(1/p_i) \leq l_i < 1 + \log_2(1/p_i)$$

3. Calculate

$$F_i = \sum_{j=0,(i-1)} p_j$$

and represent F_i as a binary fraction.
4. Then S_i is represented by the first l_i bits of F_i.

Thus, for an example, consider eight source symbols, S_1 to S_8, with probabilities as listed in the first column of Table A.1. Then l_i, F_i, and the binary representation of S_i can be read from the second, third, and fourth columns, respectively.

It can be seen that this encoding produces an immediate code because the length is such that for each new S_i the last bit is changed. It is also clear that

$$L = \sum p_i l_i$$

is bounded by

$$\sum p_i \log_2(1/p_i) \leq L < \sum p_i + \sum p_i \log_2(1/p_i)$$

So

$$H(S) \leq L < 1 + H(S)$$

In the above example $H(S) = 2.73$, while $L = 2.78$.

Table A.1

	p_i	l_i	F_i	Bit String Representation
S_1	1/4	2	0.00000	00
S_2	1/4	2	0.01000	01
S_3	1/8	3	0.10000	100
S_4	1/8	3	0.10100	101
S_5	3/32	4	0.11000	1100
S_6	1/16	4	0.11011	1101
S_7	1/16	4	0.11101	1110
S_8	1/32	5	0.11111	11111

This method of "Shannon encoding" is not the best available. For example, Huffman encoding applied to the above example would give $L = 2.75$. For our purposes, however, it is sufficient to note that L is bounded by $H(S)$, and coding procedures can be found that give L near to this bound. The fact that this compression from length $\log_2 M$ to near $H(S)$ is possible justifies our definition of redundancy.

A.2 CORRELATED SOURCES

So far we have assumed that the source symbols are uncorrelated in time, so the symbol $S_{t,i}$ emitted at time $t(i = 1$ to $M)$ is in no way affected by the symbol $S_{(t-1),j}$ emitted at time $(t-1)$. This is seldom the case, and it is necessary to extend the concept of entropy to correlated sources.

We model a correlated source as a Markov process in which the probability of $S_{t+1,i}$ is conditioned by the *state of the process as* determined by the previous k symbols emitted, $S_{t,i1} \ S_{(t-1),i2} \cdots S_{(t-k+1),ik}$. We represent this state more concisely by $C_{t,j}^k$ (or C_j^k for short when the moment in time is irrelevant). Here j runs from 1 to M^k if the i run from 1 to M. Thus, we represent the conditional probability of $S_{t+1,i}$ given the state $C_{t,j}^k$ as

$$P\left(S_{t+1,i}|C_{t,j}^k\right)$$

The entropy of such a correlated source is defined as

$$H(S) = H(S) = \sum_j P\left(C_j^k\right)H\left(C_j^k\right) \tag{A.8}$$

where

$$H\left(C_j^k\right) = -\sum_i P\left(s_{t+1,i}|C_{t,j}^k\right)\log_2 P\left(S_{t+1,i}|C_{t,j}^k\right)$$

Thus, the entropy of the source is the average, weighted by the probability of the states, of the normal entropy associated with each state. Figure A.1 illustrates such a correlated resource with $M = 2$ and $k = 3$, so that there are eight states, as shown in Figure A.1. The transitional probabilities are also shown, so, for example, $P(1|000) = 7/8$.

It is easily shown that the probabilities and entropies of the states are as shown in Table A.2.

This gives $H(S) = 0.659$.

In reality, of course, while we may guess that a source is correlated, we do not know k. We might guess that the depth of correlation is n symbols rather than

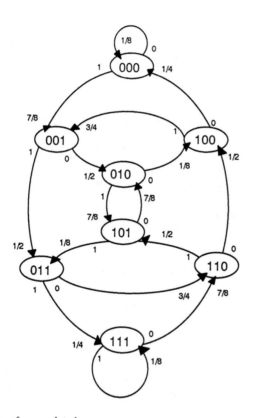

Figure A.1 State diagram of a correlated source.

Table A.2

State	000	001	010	011	100	101	110	111
Probability	2/88	7/88	28/88	7/8	7/88	28/88	7/88	2/88
Entropy	0.544	1.000	0.544	0.811	0.811	0.544	1.000	0.544

k, in which case we would work with

$$H(\bar{S}^n) = \sum_j P(C_j^n) H(C_j^n)$$

where it is assumed that the probabilities are correct, that is, those of the real process, as deduced from observation.

Theorem A.4

$$H(\bar{S}^n) \le H(\bar{S}^{n-1})$$

Proof

Clearly when $n \ge k$ $H(\bar{S}^n) = H(S)$ because of (A.8). For $n < k$

$$H(C_j^n) = - \sum_i P(S_{t+1,i}|C_{t,j}^n)\log_2 P(S_{t+1,i}|C_{t,j}^n)$$

$$\le - \sum_i P(S_{t+1,i}|C_{t,j}^n)\log_2 P(S_{t+1,i}|C_{t,j}^{n-1})$$

by Theorem A.2.
   Therefore,

$$P(C_j^n)H(C_j^n) \le - \sum_i P(S_{t+1,i}, S_{t,i1} \ldots S_{t-n+1,in})\log_2 P(S_{t+1,i}|C_{t,j}^{n-1})$$

Summing over all M^n values of j we get

$$H(\bar{S}^n) \le H(\bar{S}^{n-1}) \tag{A.9}$$

We can also consider n symbols at a time and ignore the correlation. This means that the source is regarded as an uncorrelated source of M^k symbols. We designate such a source as S^n, and its entropy is called $H(S^n)$.

Theorem A.5

$$H(S^n) = H(\bar{S}^{n-1}) + H(S^{n-1})$$

Proof

By definition

$$H(S^n) = - \sum_j P(C_j^n)\log_2 P(C_j^n)$$

$$= - \sum_j P(C_j^n)\left[\log_2 P(S_{t,i}|C_{t-1,j}^{n-1}) + \log_2 P(C_{t-1,j}^{n-1})\right]$$

$$= - \sum_j P(C_{t-1,j}^{n-1})\sum_i P(S_{t,i}|C_{t-1,j}^{n-1})\log_2 P(S_{t,i}|C_{t-1,j}^{n-1})$$

$$- \sum_j \sum_i P(S_{t,i}, C_{t-1,j}^{n-1})\log_2 P(C_{t-1,j}^{n-1})$$

So

$$H(S_n) = H(\bar{S}^{n-1}) + H(S^{n-1}) \tag{A.10}$$

Theorem A.6

$H(S^n)/n$ tends to $H(S)$ as n becomes large.

Proof

For $n \geq k$ (the correlation length) we sum equations (A.10) together, remembering that

$$H(\bar{S}^i) = H(S) \quad \text{for } i \geq k \quad \text{and } H(\bar{S}^i) \leq H(\bar{S}^1)$$

by Theorem A.4, and get

$$(n-1)H(S) + H(S^1) \leq H(S^n) \leq (k-1)H(\bar{S}^1) + (n-k)H(S) + H(S^1)$$

Dividing by n gives

$$H(S) + \left[H(S^1) - H(S)\right]/n \leq H(S^n)/n$$

$$\leq H(S) + \left[(k-1)H(\bar{S}^1) + H(S^1) - kH(S)\right]/n$$

Now

$$H(\bar{S}^1) = -\sum_j P(C^1_{t,j}) \sum_i P(S_{t+1,i}|C^1_{t,j})\log_2 P(S_{t+1,i}|C^1_{t,j})$$

$$\leq -\sum_j P(C^1_{t,j}) \sum_i P(S_{t+1,i}|C^1_{t,j})\log_2 P(S_{t+1,i})$$

by Theorem A.2. That gives

$$H(\bar{S}^1) \leq -\sum_i P(S_{t+1,i})\log_2 P(S_{t+1,i})$$

$$= H(S^1)$$

and since $H(\bar{S}^1) \geq H(S)$, the above inequality for $H(S^n)/n$ becomes

$$H(S) + a/n \leq H(S^n)/n \leq H(S) + ka/n \qquad (\text{A.11})$$

with $a \geq 0$. Therefore, $H(S^n)/n$ tends to $H(S)$ as n tends to infinity. We can also show the next theorem.

Theorem A.7

$H(S^n)/n$ decreases as n increases

Proof

$$H(S^n)\big/n - H(S^{n+1})\big/(n+1)$$

$$= \left[\sum_{i=1,n-1} H(\bar{S}^i) + H(S^1)\right]\bigg/n - \left[\sum_{i=1,n} H(\bar{S}^i) + H(S^1)\right]\bigg/(n+1)$$

$$= \left[\sum_{i=1,n-1} H(\bar{S}^i) + H(S^1)\right]\bigg/n(n+1) - H(\bar{S}^n)\big/(n+1)$$

$$= \left[\sum_{i=1,n-1} H(\bar{S}^i) + H(S^1) - nH(\bar{S}^n)\right]\bigg/n(n+1)$$

$$\geq 0$$

Therefore, $H(S^n)/n$ decreases as n increases and, by Theorem A.6, tends to $H(S)$.

We can conclude from these theorems that modelling the source as a Markov source will give better and better approximations to the real entropy as n increases to k (Theorem A.4). But, more important, if we do *not* model the correlation but group the symbols n at a time into "supersymbols" from an alphabet of M^n symbols and treat them as independent of each other in time, then the entropy per symbol $H(S^n)/n$ tends to the real entropy. This then is a justification for continuing to use compression techniques based on uncorrelated symbol strings, provided they are applied to symbols grouped n at a time. We see also that Theorem A.3 holds with the new definition of entropy, $H(S)$, if we consider variable length encoding of our supersymbol strings of n symbols.

In our specific example these theorems are illustrated by noting that

$$H(\bar{S}^1) = 0.731 \geq H(\bar{S}^2) = 0.730 \geq H(\bar{S}^3) = 0.659 = H(S)$$
$$H(S^1) = 1 \geq H(S^2)/2 = 0.866 \geq H(S^3)/3 = 0.821 \geq H(S^4)/4 = 0.780$$

and

$$H(S^2) = 1.732 = H(S^1) + H(\bar{S}^1)$$
$$H(S^3) = 2.463 = H(S^2) + H(\bar{S}^2)$$
$$H(S^4) = 3.120 = H(S^3) + H(\bar{S}^3)$$

A.3 INFORMATION IN TRANSIT

We have seen how the information generated by a source, $nH(S)$, is generally less than the number of bits, $n \log_2 M$; if there are M symbols in the alphabet, $H(S)$ is the average information content of each symbol in bits, and n symbols are sent.

The *information rate* is, therefore, $[H(S)]r$ bits per second, where r is the symbol rate, that is, the number of symbols per second.

When this information is actually transmitted, it may become subject to further losses, due to errors. We model this by considering the probabilities of transmitted symbols x_i ($i = 1$ to K) after observing received symbols y_j ($j = 1$ to K), which are the x_i with some corruptions. See Figure A.2. The symbols here are the representational symbols of the restricted alphabet into which the source symbols are encoded. $K = 2$ normally. The information associated with x_i given y_j is $-\log_2 p(x_i|y_j)$, where $p(x_i|y_j)$ is the a posteriori probability of x_i, having observed y_j. We may define

$$H(X|y_j) = -\sum_i p(x_i|y_j)\log_2 p(x_i|y_j)$$

as the average uncertainty about the source symbols remaining after viewing y_j.

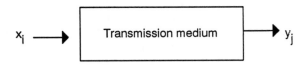

Figure A.2 Symbols being transmitted and corrupted.

Averaging over all y_j we get

$$H(X|Y) = - \sum_j p(y_j) \sum_i p(x_i|y_j)\log_2 p(x_i|y_j)$$

$$= - \sum_j \sum_i p(x_i, y_j)\left[\log_2 p(x_i, y_j) - \log_2 p(y_j)\right] \quad \text{(A.12)}$$

$$H(X|Y) = H(X,Y) - H(Y)$$

Equation (A.12) may be interpreted as follows:

> The residual uncertainty about the inputs X to a channel after viewing the outputs Y is the joint uncertainties of X and Y (before doing any viewing) *less* the information obtained (uncertainty removed) by viewing Y.

$H(X|Y)$ has been called by Shannon the "equivocation". In practice we are more likely to know $p(y_j|x_i)$, the probability of x_i being corrupted to y_j, than $p(x_i|y_j)$, but the one may be calculated from the other by using Bayes's theorem. Thus,

$$p(x_i|y_j) = p(y_j|x_i)p(x_i)/p(y_j)$$

with

$$p(y_j) = \sum_{i=1, K} p(y_j|x_i)p(x_i)$$

If the channel is error free, we have

$$p(y_j|x_i) = 1 \quad \text{if } j = i$$

$$= 0 \quad \text{if } j \neq i$$

For another example, suppose that the probability of corruption of x_i is p, and that corruption turns x_i into $y_j (j \neq i)$ equally over the y_j, then

$$p(y_j|x_i) = 1 - p \qquad \text{if } j = i$$

$$= p/(K - 1) \quad \text{if } j \neq i \qquad \text{(A.13)}$$

By using the model of (A.13) for our channel and making the additional assumption that all x_i are equally probable, so that

$$p(x_i) = 1/K$$

it is easy to show that

$$p(y_j) = 1/K$$

and

$$p(x_i, y_j) = (1-p)/K \qquad \text{if } j = i$$
$$= p/K(K-1) \qquad \text{if } j \neq i$$

and so calculate the equivocation

$$H(X|Y) = H(p) + p \log_2(K-1) \tag{A.14}$$

where $H(p)$ is the entropy function of p.

Note that the assumption that the x_i $(i = 1$ to $K)$ are equally probable will be true if we have compressed the M source symbols down to $H(S) \log_K 2$ representational symbols, where $H(S)$ is the source entropy measured in bits; that is, when redundancy is removed from the information prior to transmission. When $K = 2$ (A.14) becomes

$$H(X|Y) = H(p) \tag{A.15}$$

We now consider the quantity $I(X:Y)$ called the *mutual information* and defined by

$$I(X:Y) = H(X) - H(X|Y) \tag{A.16}$$
$$= -\sum_i p(x_i) \log_2 p(x_i) + \sum_j p(y_j) \sum_i p(x_i|y_j) \log_2 p(x_i|y_j)$$
$$= -\sum_i \sum_j p(x_i, y_j) \left[\log_2 p(x_i) - \log_2 p(x_i|y_j) \right]$$
$$= -\sum_i \sum_j p(x_i, y_j) \left[\log_2 (p(x_i)p(y_j)) - \log_2 p(x_i, y_j) \right] \tag{A.17}$$
$$\geq 0 \text{ by Theorem 2}$$

The definition of the mutual information shows that it is *the information about X conveyed by the channel*, because it is the a priori uncertainty about X less the a posteriori uncertainty having viewed the output Y. Furthermore the symmetry of (A.17) shows that $I(X:Y) = I(Y:X)$ or

$$I(X:Y) = H(Y) - H(Y|X) \tag{A.18}$$

(A.18) is often a more convenient expression to work with than (A.16). For example, if we assume that for i fixed

$$p(y_j|x_i) = q_j, \left(\sum_j q_j = 1 \right)$$

and that as we vary i the *values* q_j do not change, although they may be permuted so that a given q_j may be associated with a y_k ($k \neq j$), then we have a channel that is known as "uniform from the input", that is, the value of x_i does not affect the pattern of corruption. For such a channel $H(Y|x_i)$ is an expression in the q_j, into which x_i does not enter, so that

$$H(Y|X) = \sum_i p(x_i) H(Y|x_i)$$

is independent of the input X.

In this case, as X varies, $I(X:Y)$ varies only as determined by $H(Y)$, as can be seen from (A.18).

We now define the *capacity, C, of the channel* as the maximum value of $I(X:Y)$ as we alter the inputs X. That is, we select our inputs so as to minimise their liability to error on the channel. Clearly, from (A.18) and assuming uniformity from the input applies, $I(X:Y)$ is maximised when $H(Y)$ is maximised, and we know that occurs when $p(y_j) = 1/K$. If, in addition, we assume that $p(y_j)$ runs through all the K values of q_j as x_i changes, then we can make $p(y_j) = 1/K$ if we have $p(x_i) = 1/K$ because

$$p(y_j) = \sum_i p(y_j|x_i) p(x_i)$$

$$= \sum_k q_k/K$$

$$= 1/K$$

In this case we have

$C = H(Y) - H(Y|X)$ maximised

$= \log_2 K - \sum_j q_j \log_2(1/q_j)$

$= \log_2 K - \{(1-p)\log_2[1/(1-p)]\} + [(K-1)(p/(K-1))]\log_2((K-1)/p)\}$

$= \log_2 K - H(p) - p \log_2(K-1)$

$[= H(X) - H(X|Y)$ from (A.14)$]$

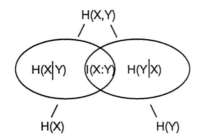

Figure A.3 Relationship between equivocation, mutual information, etc.

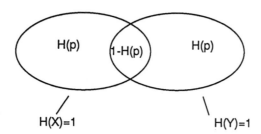

Figure A.4 Equivocation and mutual information for the BSC.

where we have taken the q_j to be $(1-p)$ and $(K-1)$ values of $p/(K-1)$, corresponding to our uniformity from the input and other assumptions. In the specific case where $K = 2$, which is that of the *binary symmetric channel (BSC)*, where p is the probability of a bit being changed from 0 to 1 or from 1 to 0, we have

$$C = 1 - H(p) \qquad (A.19)$$

Thus, the capacity, the maximum information-carrying capability, of the BSC is determined by (A.19) and is achieved when the input bits 0 and 1 are equally likely, as will be the case if the input information is nonredundant. The residual uncertainty or equivocation $H(X|Y)$ is then $H(p)$ [see (A.15)]. The capacity is unity when $p = 0$ and the equivocation is zero. The capacity is zero when $p = 1/2$.

Assuming then that we have a source of M symbols at a rate of r symbols per second and that these are compressed to $H(S)$ bits giving an information rate of $H(S)r$ bits per second, on reception from the BSC we will have an information rate of $H(S)[1 - H(p)]r$ bits per second.

The relationship between the various quantities $H(X|Y)$, $H(X,Y)$, $I(X:Y)$, and so on, is illustrated in Figure A.3.

The specific case of the BSC is illustrated in Figure A.4, with the assumption that $p(x_i) = 1/2$, $x_i = 0$ or 1.

$$S < (p/\alpha)^{\alpha n}[(1-p)/(1-\alpha)]^{(1-\alpha)n} K \qquad \text{(B.1)}$$

th $K = \alpha(1-p)/(\alpha-p)\sqrt{[2\pi n(1-\alpha)]}$, which tends to 0 for large n.
Now the expression

$$(p/\alpha)^{n}[(1-p)/(1-\alpha)]^{(1-\alpha)n}$$

as, for $\alpha > p$, a minimum value of 0 (when $p = 0$) and a maximum value of 1
when $p = \alpha$) and increases monotonically between these values as p increases
om 0 to α, as can be seen by differentiation.
    Therefore, for large n, S tends to zero. This means that

$$\sum_{i=0,(n\alpha-1)} \binom{n}{i} p^{i}(1-p)^{n-i} = 1 - S \text{ tends to 1 for large } n$$

f $\alpha > p$.
    With $\beta = \alpha - 1/n$ and $\beta > p - 1/n$, we have

$$\sum_{i=0,\beta n} \binom{n}{i} p^{i}(1-p)^{n-i} \text{ tends to 1 for large } n \qquad \text{(B.2)}$$

If p is the probability of a bit error, (B.2) states that for β large enough, effectively
the probability of error patterns, including more than βn errors, tends to 0 as n
increases.
    If we put $p = 1/2$ in inequality (B.1) and, for large n, take $K < 1$, we have

$$S < (1/\alpha)^{\alpha n}[1/(1-\alpha)]^{(1-\alpha)n}/2^{n}$$

Therefore, $\log_2 S < nH(\alpha) - n = n[H(\alpha) - 1]$
    So

$$S < 2^{-n[1-H(\alpha)]}$$

But with $p = 1/2$,

$$S = \sum_{i=\alpha n,n} \binom{n}{i} \Big/ 2^{n} = \sum_{i=0,n(1-\alpha)} \binom{n}{i} \Big/ 2^{n}$$

Appendix B
Some Binomial Approximations

Consider the sum

$$S = \sum_{i=\alpha n, n} k_i$$

where $k_i = \binom{n}{i} p^i (1-p)^{n-i}$.

Thus, S is the probability of (αn) or more binomially distributed the individual probability is p.

$$k_{i+1}/k_i = p(n-i)/(1-p)(i+1) = \beta_i$$

β_i decreases as i increases.

The starting value for β_i is when $i = \alpha n$, and then

$$\beta_{\alpha n} = pn(1-\alpha)/(1-p)(\alpha n + 1) < p(1-\alpha)/\alpha(1-p) = \beta$$

If $\alpha > p$, then $\beta < 1$.

Since each term of S is less than its predecessor by at least a fact have

$$S < \sum_{i=0}^{n-\alpha n} \beta^i \binom{n}{\alpha n} p^{\alpha n} (1-p)^{n-\alpha n}$$

$$= (1 - \beta^{n(1-\alpha)}) \binom{n}{\alpha n} p^{\alpha n} (1-p)^{n-\alpha n} / (1-\beta)$$

$$< \binom{n}{\alpha n} p^{\alpha n} (1-p)^{n-\alpha n} (1-p)\alpha/(\alpha - p)$$

Now by Stirling's formula

$$\binom{n}{\alpha n} \leq \alpha^{-n\alpha} (1-\alpha)^{-n(1-\alpha)} / \sqrt{[2\pi n(1-\alpha)]}$$

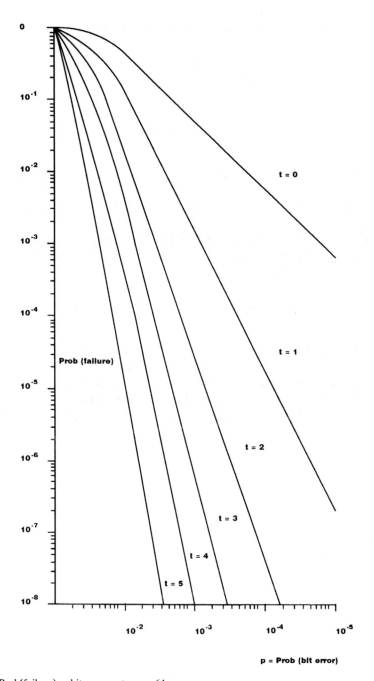

Figure B.1 Prob(failure) v. bit-error-rate, $n = 64$.

because the binomial coefficients are symmetric; therefore,

$$\sum_{i=0,\,n(1-\alpha)} \binom{n}{i} \Big/ 2^n = S < 2^{-n(1-H(\alpha))}$$

or

$$\sum_{i=0,\,n\beta} \binom{n}{i} < 2^{nH(\beta)}$$

(B.3)

with $\beta = (1 - \alpha)$, because the entropy function is also symmetric, $H(\alpha) = H(1 - \alpha)$.

Inequality (B.3) holds for $\alpha > p = 1/2$, or $\beta < 1/2$, as n becomes large. It is a useful bound on the sum of the binomial coefficients, for example, in proving Shannon's theorem.

Returning to (B.2), we can define the Prob(Failure), the probability of an error-correction failure owing to the presence of more than t errors, where $d = 2t + 1$ is the distance of the code, as

$$\text{Prob(Failure)} = 1 - \sum_{i=0,\,t} \binom{n}{i} p^i (1-p)^{n-i}$$

with $t = n\beta$. As discussed, this tends to zero as n increases provided $\beta > p$. We can also hold n and t constant and plot the Prob(Failure) against decreasing p to produce the so-called "waterfall curves". Figure B.1 shows such curves for $n = 64$, $t = 1$ to 20. Note that we do not state that there exist codes with these values of n and t, but if there did they would have error-correcting capabilities of Figure B.1.

Appendix C
Finite Fields

A field is a set of elements over which the operations of addition, subtraction, multiplication, and division are defined. There exist the following identity elements:

- The additive identity element 0 such that if x is any field element $x + 0 = 0 + x = x$;
- The multiplicative identity element 1 such that if x is any field element $x \cdot 1 = 1 \cdot x = x$

In a field every element x has an additive inverse $-x$ such that $x + (-x) = (-x) + x = 0$.

In a field every nonzero element x also has a multiplicative inverse x^{-1} such that $x \cdot x^{-1} = x^{-1} \cdot x = 1$. Also $x \cdot 0 = 0 \cdot x = 0$. Thus, all the field elements form an additive group, and the nonzero elements form a multiplicative group.

Fields may have an infinite or a finite number of elements. If the field is finite, repeated additions or multiplications of an element to or by itself of necessity result in the original element again after k operations, say. Therefore, after $(k - 1)$ operations the result must have been the identity element (additive or multiplicative). In the particular case of repeated addition of the multiplicative identity, if

$$1 + 1 + 1 + \cdots + 1 = 0 \quad \text{after } p \text{ operations (but not before)}$$

we say that "the finite field has characteristic p". A finite field with q elements is called "GF(q)".

The following theorems summarise the main properties of finite fields.

Theorem C.1

The characteristic of the field, p, is prime.

Proof

If $p = x \cdot y$, then $(x \cdot 1)(y \cdot 1) = p \cdot 1 = 0$, where $(n \cdot 1)$ means 1 added to itself n times. But this implies $(x \cdot 1)^{-1}(x \cdot 1)(y \cdot 1) = 0$ which implies $y \cdot 1 = 0$ with $y < p$, which is a contradiction because p, the characteristic, is the smallest n such that $n \cdot 1 = 0$. Therefore, p is prime.

Theorem C.2

The number of elements is p^m.

Proof

Consider $0, 1, 2, \ldots, (p - 1)$.

- If there exists another element α, we have p^2 elements $(i + j\alpha)$ $i, j = 0$ to $p - 1$.
- If $\alpha^2 \neq i_1 + j_1\alpha$ for some i_1, j_1, then we have p^3 elements $(i + j\alpha + k\alpha^2)$, and so on.
- If, however, $\alpha^2 = i_1 + j_1\alpha$, consider $\beta \neq i_2 + j_2\alpha$ for any i_2, j_2, and we have p^3 elements. Continuing in this way, we get p^m elements of the form $\Sigma i_k \alpha^{i1} \beta^{i2}$, and so on.

Theorem C.3

A polynomial $q(x)$ of degree n over a finite field (i.e., with coefficients from the finite field) has at most n roots.

Proof

Assume this is true for $(n - 1)$. If there exists no root α of $q(x)$, then there is nothing to prove. If α is a root, then we can divide $q(x)$ by $(x - \alpha)$ and get $q(x) = (x - \alpha) s(x) + r$. (Division is possible because the coefficients form a field.) Now $r = 0$ if α is a root, and $s(x)$ has $\leq n - 1$ roots by hypothesis; therefore, $q(x)$ has $\leq n$ roots.

Theorem C.4

Given that there are p^m elements in the field, all nonzero elements satisfy $x^{p^m - 1} = 1$, and since there are $(p^m - 1)$ of them the roots of $(x^{p^m - 1} - 1)$ are all distinct and define the field.

Proof

The powers of any element α form a cyclic subgroup of order e (i.e., $\alpha^e = 1$ and $\alpha^f \neq 1$ for any $f < e$). By considering multiplicative cosets of this subgroup, we see that e divides $(p^m - 1)$. Therefore, $x^{p^m - 1} = 1$ for all elements.

Theorem C.5

If α, β have orders d, e, which are coprime, then order$(\alpha\beta) = de$.

Proof

1. Let order$(\alpha\beta) = f$, that is, $(\alpha\beta)^f = 1$.
   Now $(\alpha\beta)^{de} = (\alpha^d)^e(\beta^e)^d = 1$.
   Therefore, f divides de.
2. But $1 = (\alpha\beta)^{fd} = (\alpha^d)^f(\beta)^{fd} = \beta^{fd}$.
   Therefore, e divides fd.
   But since e, d are coprime, e divides f.
   Similarly d divides f.
   Therefore, since e, f are coprime, ed divides f.
3. Therefore, from 1 and 2, $f = de$.

Theorem C.6

There exists a primitive element γ among the $(p^m - 1)$ nonzero elements of the GF(p^m), such that $\gamma^e = 1$ for $e = p^m - 1$, but for no smaller value of e.

Proof

Let $p^m - 1 = p_1^{e1} p_2^{e2} \ldots p_k^{ek}$. Let $q = (p^m - 1)/p1$. There exist elements in the field that do not satisfy $x^q = 1$ (by Theorem C.3). Let α_1 be such an element, with Order $= p_1^{f1} p_2^{f2} \ldots p_k^{fk}$. Then $f_1 = e_1$ (otherwise, $\prod p_i^{fi}$ divides q, a contradiction). Therefore, α_1 raised to the power $p_2^{f2} p_3^{f3} \ldots p_k^{fk}$ has order p_1^{e1}. Similarly we find α_2 of order p_2^{e2}, and so on. Then $\gamma = \prod \alpha_i$ has order $\prod p_i^{ei}$ (by Theorem C.5), and $\prod p_i^{ei} = p^m - 1$.

Theorem C.7

All finite fields GF(p^m) are of the form

$$\sum_{i=0,\,m-1} a_i \gamma^i \quad \text{with} \quad \sum_{i=0,\,m} b_i \gamma^i = 0$$

with a_i, b_i in GF(p).

Proof

If γ is chosen primitive $\gamma^j \neq$ any $\sum_{i<j} a_i \gamma^i$ provided $j \leq m - 1$, because that would imply only p^j distinct powers of γ. When $j = m$, we must have

$$\sum_{i=0,\,m} b_i \gamma^i = 0$$

otherwise, the field would have too many elements.

Theorem C.8

If $q(x)$ is an irreducible polynomial, over GF(p), of degree d with a root α, then other roots are $\alpha^p, \alpha^{p^2} \ldots \alpha^{p^{d-1}}$, all are distinct, and $q(x)$ divides $(x^{p^d-1} - 1)$.

Proof

$q(\alpha) = 0$, so $[q(\alpha)]^p = 0$. But $[q(\alpha)]^p = q(\alpha^p)$, since cross terms are zero. Therefore, α^p is a root of $q(x)$. Therefore, $(\alpha^p)^p = \alpha^{p^2}$ is a root, and so on. Suppose $\alpha p^j = \alpha p^i$. Some $j > i$. Then $\alpha p^i(p^r - 1) = 1$ with $r = j - i$. But order(α) divides $(p^m - 1)$. Therefore, $i = 0$, and we have order(α) $= p^r - 1$.
But the roots of $(x^{p^r-1} - 1)$ (plus 0) define a field, GF(p^r), by Theorem C.6, and α is in this field, so α must satisfy a polynomial over GF(p) of degree r or less, with other roots $\alpha^p, \alpha^{p^2}, \ldots \alpha^{p^{r-1}}$. This implies that $q(x)$ is not irreducible, a contradiction; therefore, all roots are distinct and $j = r = d$. Finally, since $\alpha, \alpha^p, \alpha^{p^2} \ldots \alpha^{p^{d-1}}$ are in the field composed of roots of $(x^{p^d-1} - 1)$ (plus 0) $q(x)$ divides $(x^{p^d-1} - 1)$

Theorem C.9

All the roots $\alpha, \alpha^p, \alpha^{p^2} \ldots \alpha^{p^{d-1}}$ of $q(x)$ have the same order, and if α is primitive all roots are primitive, and $q(x)$ is a *primitive* polynomial.

Proof

Let order$(\alpha) = e$, order$(\alpha^p) = f$. $(\alpha^p)^e = (\alpha^e)^p = 1$. So f divides e. $1 = (\alpha^p)^f = \alpha^{pf}$. So e divides (pf). But e divides $(p^d - 1)$ since $\alpha^{p^d-1} = 1$. Therefore, e cannot have a factor p. So e divides f. Therefore, $e = f$, since f divides e and e divides f.

Theorem C.10

Every element α in GF(p^m) has a minimum polynomial $m_\alpha(x)$ of degree d_α, and $m_\alpha(x)$ divides $(x^{p^{d_\alpha-1}} - 1)$ and $m_\alpha(x)$ divides $(x^{p^m-1} - 1)$.

Proof

1. $m_\alpha(x)$ exists (Theorem C.2).
2. $m_\alpha(x)$ is unique; otherwise, if there were two minimum polynomials of degree d_α, their difference would also have a root α and be of lower degree.
3. $m_\alpha(x)$ divides $(x^{p^{d_\alpha-1}} - 1)$ by Theorem C.8.
4. Since the roots of $m_\alpha(x)$ are also in GF(p^m) being α^{p^i}, $m_\alpha(x)$ divides $(x^{p^m-1} - 1)$ by Theorem C.4.

Theorem C.11

If $q(x)$ is irreducible of degree d, and $q(x)$ divides $(x^{p^m-1} - 1)$ then $(p^d - 1)$ divides $(p^m - 1)$.

Proof

The elements

$$\sum_{i=0}^{d-1} a_i \alpha^i$$

where a_i is in GF(p) and α is a root of $q(x)$, form a field. The nonzero elements form a multiplicative group of order($p^d - 1$), which is a subgroup of the multiplicative group of GF(p^m) (less 0), because α is in GF(p^m).

Therefore, ($p^d - 1$) divides ($p^m - 1$).

Theorem C.12

($p^d - 1$) divides ($p^m - 1$) if and only if d divides m; consequently, minimum polynomials have degree d, which divides m (by Theorem C.11).

Proof

Let $m = kd + j$, $j < d$.

$$p^m = \left(p^d - 1\right)\left(p^{m-d} + p^{m-2d} + \cdots + p^{m-kd}\right) + p^j.$$

Therefore, $(p^m - 1) = (p^d - 1)(p^{m-d} + p^{m-2d} + \cdots + p^{m-kd}) + p^j - 1$. Therefore, if $j = 0$, ($p^d - 1$) divides ($p^m - 1$).

Conversely, if ($p^d - 1$) divides ($p^m - 1$), $j = 0$ because ($p^d - 1$) does not divide ($p^j - 1$).

Theorem C.13

If $q(x)$ is irreducible of degree d and d divides m, then $q(x)$ divides ($x^{p^d-1} - 1$) divides ($x^{p^m-1} - 1$). Consequently, the roots of $q(x)$ are in GF(p^m), so all irreducible polynomials of degree d dividing m lie in GF(p^m).

Proof

$q(x)$ divides ($x^{p^d-1} - 1$) by Theorem C.8. ($x^r - 1$) divides ($x^s - 1$) if and only if r divides s by a similar proof to that of Theorem C.12, so if $r = p^d - 1$, $s = p^m - 1$ and d divides m, then r divides s and ($x^r - 1$) divides ($x^s - 1$).

Theorem C.14

If α is in GF(p^m) and has minimum polynomial $m(x)$ of degree d, then α^i has minimum polynomial of degree e dividing d.

Proof

α^i is in field GF(p^d). Therefore, by Theorem C.12, e divides d.

Theorem C.15

If $\Pi(d)$ = Number of irreducible polynomials of degree d (d divides m), then $p^m - 1 = \Sigma d\Pi(d)$, and $(x^{p^{m-1}} - 1)$ = Product (all irreducible polynomials of degree d), where d divides m.

Proof

By Theorem C.13 all irreducible polynomials of degree d dividing m divide $(x^{p^{m-1}} - 1)$, so all the roots are in the field. Therefore, $p^m - 1 \geq \Sigma d\Pi(d)$, where d divides m. By Theorem C.12 any element not accounted for has a minimum polynomial of degree d dividing m, but since *all* irreducible polynomials of degree d dividing m have been included, $p^m - 1 = \Sigma d\Pi(d)$ for d dividing m.

Theorem C.16

If m = prime, the $\Pi(m) = (p^m - p)/m$.

Proof

If m is prime, the divisors of m are $d = 1, m$
$\Pi(1) = (p - 1)$. Therefore, $p^m - 1 = 1 \cdot (p - 1) + m\Pi(m)$ by Theorem C.15.
    Therefore, $\Pi(m) = (p^m - p)/m$.

Theorem C.17

Any irreducible polynomial of degree m defines a field GF(p^m), but there exists only one such field.

Proof

The field is defined by the solution to $(x^{p^{m-1}} - 1) = 0$ whose factorisation is unique by Theorem C.15 so that the field is unique, and it depends only on which minimum polynomial of degree m we choose for definition.

Theorem C.18

The number of primitive polynomials of degree m is $\phi(p^m - 1)/m$, where $\phi(\ )$ is Euler's totient function.

Proof

If α has order d in $GF(p^m)$. Then $\text{order}(\alpha^j) = e = d/[hcf\ (j, d)] = d/h$, say, because $(\alpha^j)^{d/h} = (\alpha^d)^{j/h} = 1$. So e divides d/h.

And if $1 = (\alpha^j)^e = \alpha^{je}$, then d divides je. So if $d = xh$, $j = yh$ we have x divides e, or (d/h) divides e. Therefore, $e = d/h$.

So if γ is primitive with order $d = p^m - 1$. There exist $\phi(p^m - 1)$ values of j such that γ^j is primitive and each satisfies a polynomial of degree m.

Therefore, there exist $\phi(p^m - 1)/m$ primitive polynomials of degree m over $GF(p^m)$.

Appendix D

The Berlekamp-Massey Algorithm

The algorithm is used to solve for the f_i the set of equations:

$$S_{j+r} + f_1 S_{j+r-1} + f_2 S_{j+r-2} + \cdots + f_{r-1} S_{j+1} + f_r S_j = 0$$

for $j = 1$ to $(2t - r)$ with $r \le t$. The value of t is known, but the value of r is not known. It is known, however, that if we guess a value s for r and $s < r$, then the equations will be inconsistent due to the way the S_i are constructed, and the system will have no solution (see Section 4.4).

The algorithm, therefore, uses an approach in which r is first assumed to be 1 and f_1 is chosen so that $S_2 + f_1 S_1 = 0$. Then tests are made for increasing $n = 3$ to $2t$ to see if $S_n + f_1 S_{n-1} = 0$. If these tests succeed, we conclude that $r = 1$; otherwise, we introduce new "prediction" coefficients f_1 and f_2 (derived from the old f_1) such that $S_3 + f_1 S_2 + f_2 S_1 = 0$ and test whether $S_n + f_1 S_{n-1} + f_2 S_{n-2} = 0$ for $n = 4$ to $2t$. If these tests succeed, we conclude $r = 2$; otherwise, we try f_1, f_2, f_3 and $(S_n + f_1 S_{n-1} + f_2 S_{n-2} + f_3 S_{n-3})$ for $n = 5$ to $2t$, and so on. In fact the algorithm is more clever than indicated and can skip some unnecessary trial values for r under certain circumstances.

In the algorithm we use a polynomial $g(x) = x^r f(1/x)$, where $f(x)$ is as defined in Section 4.4, namely, $f(x) = x^r + f_1 x^{r-1} + \cdots + f_{r-1} x + f_r$, so that

$$g(x) = 1 + f_1 x + f_2 x^2 + \cdots + f_r x^r$$

The algorithm is as follows:

1. Initialise $g(x) = 1$, the correction polynomial $c(x) = x$, $n = 1$ and $r = 0$.
2. Evaluate the prediction error:

$$e = S_n + \sum_{i=1,r} f_i S_{n-i}$$

3. If e is zero, go to step 8; otherwise, make adjustments to remove the error in steps 4 to 6.

---

4. Set $g^*(x) = g(x) - ec(x)$.

   This forms a new predictor polynomial that satisfies the equations up to the current value corresponding to n, namely, S_n.

5. If $2r \geq n$, go to step 7.

   There are $(n - r)$ equations in r unknowns, so if $2r \geq n$ there is no problem of inconsistency.

6. Set $r = (n - r)$ and $c(x) = g(x)/e$.

   There are too few unknowns for the $(n - r)$ equations, so increase them to accommodate $g^*(x)$ and establish a new correction polynomial that leaves all equations up to $(n - 1)$ satisfied and normalises the error for the last equation.

7. Set $g(x) = g^*(x)$.

8. Set $c(x) = x c(x)$.

9. Set $n = n + 1$.

10. If $n \leq 2t$, go to step 2; otherwise, terminate.

Applying this to the example of Section 4.4 with $S_1 = \alpha^2$, $S_2 = \alpha^4$, $S_3 = 0$, $S_4 = \alpha^8$, $S_5 = \alpha^{10}$, $S_6 = 0$, where $t = 3$, and α is a root of $x^4 + x + 1$ over GF(2), we get the following iterations.

FIRST ITERATION

1. $g(x) = 1$, $c(x) = x$, $n = 1$, $r = 0$
2. $e = S_1 = \alpha^2$
4. $g^*(x) = 1 + \alpha^2 x$(over GF(2) $\alpha^2 = -\alpha^2$)
6. $r = 1$, $c(x) = 1/\alpha^2$
7. $g(x) = 1 + \alpha^2 x$
8. $c(x) = x/\alpha^2$
9. $n = 2$

SECOND ITERATION

2. $e = S_2 + \alpha^2 S_1 = \alpha^4 + \alpha^4 = 0$
8. $c(x) = x^2/\alpha^2 = \alpha^{13} x^2$
9. $n = 3$

THIRD ITERATION

2. $e = S_3 + \alpha^2 S_2 = 0 + \alpha^6 = \alpha^6$
4. $g^*(x) = 1 + \alpha^2 x + \alpha^6 (x^2/\alpha^2) = 1 + \alpha^2 x + \alpha^4 x^2$
6. $r = 2$, $c(x) = (1 + \alpha^2 x)/\alpha^6 = \alpha^9 + \alpha^{11} x$
7. $g(x) = 1 + \alpha^2 x + \alpha^4 x^2$
8. $c(x) = \alpha^9 x + \alpha^{11} x^2$
9. $n = 4$

FOURTH ITERATION

2. $e = S_4 + \alpha^2 S_3 + \alpha^4 S_2 = \alpha^8 + 0 + \alpha^8 = 0$
8. $c(x) = \alpha^9 x^2 + \alpha^{11} x^3$
9. $n = 5$

FIFTH ITERATION

2. $e = S_5 + \alpha^2 S_4 + \alpha^4 S_3 = \alpha^{10} + \alpha^{10} + 0 = 0$
8. $c(x) = \alpha^9 x^3 + \alpha^{11} x^4$
9. $n = 6$

SIXTH ITERATION

2. $e = S_6 + \alpha^2 S_5 + \alpha^4 S_4 = 0 + \alpha^{12} + \alpha^{12} = 0$
8. $c(x) = \alpha^9 x^4 + \alpha^{11} x^5$
9. $n = 7$
10. Terminate
    We end with $r = 2$, $g(x) = 1 + \alpha^2 x + \alpha^4 x^2$ or $f_1 = \alpha^2$, $f_2 = \alpha^4$ and all four equations $(S_n + f_1 S_{n-1} + f_2 S_{n-2} = 0)$ satisfied for $n = 3$ to 6, although there are only two free variables, f_1 and f_2.

References

[1] Shannon, C. E., "A Mathematical Theory of Communication," *Bell Systems Technical Journal*, Vol. 27, 1948.

[2] Abramson, N., *Information Theory and Coding*. New York: McGraw Hill, 1963.

[3] Hamming, R. W., "Error-Detecting and Error-Correcting Codes," *Bell Systems Technical Journal*, Vol. 29, 1950.

[4] Shannon, C. E., "Communication in the Presence of Noise," *IRE Proc.*, Vol. 37, 1949.

[5] Golay, M. J. E., "Notes on Digital Coding," *IRE Proc.*, Vol 37, 1949.

[6] Varsharmov, R. R., "Estimate of the Number of Signals in Error Correcting Codes," *Doklady A.N.S.S.S.R.*, 117, No. 5, 1957.

[7] Plotkin, M., "Binary Codes with Specified Minimum Distance," *IRE Trans.*, Vol. IT-6, 1960.

[8] CCITT Ninth Plenary Assembly Blue Book. Recommendation V.41 (Fascicle VIII.1). See also Recommendation X.25 (Fascicle VIII.2).

[9] Kasami, T., "A Decoding Procedure for Multiple Error-Correcting Codes," *IEEE Trans. on Information Theory*, Vol. IT-10, 1964.

[10] Bose, R. C., and D. K. R. Chaudhuri, "On a Class of Error-Correcting Binary Group Codes," *Inf. Control*, Vol. 3, 1960. See also A. Hocquenghem, "Codes correcteurs d'erreurs," *Chiffres.*, Vol. 2, 1959.

[11] Massey, J. L., "Shift-Register Synthesis and BCH Recoding," *IEEE Trans. on Information Theory*, Vol. IT-15, 1969.

[12] Reed, I. S., and G. Solomon, "Polynomial Codes over Certain Finite Fields," *J. SIAM.*, Vol. 8, 1960.

[13] Viterbi, A. J., "Error Bounds for Convolutional Codes and an Asymptotically Optimum Decoding Algorithm," *IEEE Trans. on Information Theory*, Vol. IT-13, 1967.

[14] Fano, R. M., "A Heuristic Discussion of Probabilistic Decoding," *IEEE Trans. on Information Theory*, Vol. IT-9, 1963.

[15] Viterbi, A. J., and J. K. Omura, *Principles of Digital Communication and Coding*. New York: McGraw Hill, 1979.

[16] Michelson, A. M., and A. H. Levesque, *Error-Control Techniques for Digital Communication*. New York: Wiley-Interscience, 1985.

[17] Peterson, W. W., and E. J. Weldon, *Error-Correcting Codes*. Cambridge, Mass.: MIT Press, 1972.

Index

BCH codes
    error correction of binary, 53–58
    error correction of nonbinary, 58–59
    examples of, 51–52
    minimum polynomials in, 47–48
    Reed-Solomon codes, 59–67
    roots of, 48–51
Berlekamp-Massey algorithm, 58, 125–27
Binary Erasure Channel, 6
Binary information units (bits), 96
Binary symmetric channel (BSC), 111
Binomial approximations, 113–16
Bit strings, 1–7
Block codes, 7
    and convolutional codes, 91–93
Bose-Chaudhuri-Hocquenghem codes.
        See BCH codes
BSC (binary symmetric channel), 111
Bursts, of errors, 6–7

Capacity, of channel, 110
Closed code, 12
Code(s)
    BCH. *See* BCH codes
    bit strings and, 1–7
    block, 7, 91–93
    closed, 12
    convolutional. *See* Convolutional codes
    cyclic. *See* Cyclic codes
    and error correction, 3–5
    Golay, 18, 38
    immediate, 97
    linear. *See* Linear codes
    perfect, 18–19
    Reed-Solomon, 29, 59–67
    repetition, 18–19

tree and trellis, 69–72
Code-distance, 7
Code rate, 8
Codevectors, 3
Codewords, 3
Columns, of null matrix, 17–18
Constraint length, 70
Convolutional codes
    analysis of, 78–81
    block codes and, 91–93
    control of decoding errors with, 77–78
    defined, 73
    error correcting with, 81–91
    feedback decoding with, 86–89
    linear, 72–78
    sequential decoding with, 85–86
    soft-decision decoding with, 84–85
    syndrome decoding with, 87–91
    tree and trellis codes, 69–72
Correlated sources, 102–107
Cosets, 12
Cyclic codes
    defined, 32
    error correction with, 42–44
    error detection with, 38–42
    generating polynomial for, 31–35
    nonbinary, 44–46
    roots of generating polynomial and null
        matrix in, 35–37
    shortened, 40–42
    systematic, 33–35
    weight distributions of, 39–40

Decoding
    feedback, 86–89
    sequential, 85–86

Decoding (*cont.*)
  soft-decision, 5–7, 84–85
  syndrome, 89–91
Decoding errors, control of, 77–78
Delay operator, 76
Detectable errors, 24–25
Distance, of linear code, 17

Entropy, 96
  of correlated source, 102
Equivocation, 108, 111
Erasures, 5–7
Error(s)
  bursts of, 6–7
  detectable, 24–25
  postdecoding, 80–81
Error correction
  with binary BCH codes, 53–58
  codes and, 3–5
  with convolutional codes, 81–91
  with cyclic codes, 42–44
  forward, 4
  with nonbinary BCH codes, 58–59
Error detection, with cyclic codes, 38–42
Error locator, 53
Error-recovery, by detection and retransmission, 4

Feedback decoding, with convolutional
      codes, 86–89
Feedback shift registers, 40–42
Field(s), 117
  finite, 11, 117–24
Forward error correction (FEC), 4

Generating polynomial, 31–35
  roots of, and null matrix, 35–37
Generator matrix, 13–14
Golay code, 18, 38

Hamming distance, 7–8

Ideal, 31
Immediate code, 97
Information
  associated with event, 95–96
  average, 96
  maximum, 96–97
  mutual, 109, 111
  in transit, 107–111
Information rate, 107
Information theory
  correlated sources in, 102–107
  information, entropy, redundancy, and
      compression in, 95–102

information in transit in, 107–11
Information units, binary, 96
Interleaved RS code, 63–64

Kasami method, 42–43

Linear codes
  bounds in practice on, 23–25
  convolutional, 72–78
  distance of, 17
  matrix representation for, 11–14
  nonbinary, 25–29
  null matrix or parity-check matrix for, 14–18
  perfect codes in, 18–19
  Plotkin bound on, 20–23
  Varsharmov-Gilbert bound on, 19–20

Matrix
  generator, 13–14
  null, 14–18
  parity, 13
  parity-check, 14–18
  representation of, 11–14
Metric, 83
Minimum polynomials, in BCH codes, 47–48
Minimum weight, 12
Mutual information, 109, 111

Nonbinary BCH codes, error correction
      of, 58–59
Nonbinary cyclic codes, 44–46
Nonbinary linear codes, 25–29
Null matrix, 14–18
  columns of, 17–18
  roots of generating polynomial and, 35–37
Nullspace, 14

Parity-check matrix, 14–18
Parity matrix, 13
Perfect codes, 18–19
Plotkin bound, 20–23
Postdecoding errors, 80–81
Preamble, 72

Redundancy, 2–3, 97
Reed-Solomon (RS) codes, 29, 59–67
  interleaved, 63–64
  nearness to bounds of, 65–67
  practical use of, 62–64
  weight distribution of, 64–65
  worked example of, 60–62
Reliability factor, 6
Repetition codes, 18–19
Residual error rate, 64
Retransmission, error-recovery by, 4

Roots
    of BCH codes, 48–51
    consecutive, 48
    of cyclic codes, 35–37
RS codes. *See* Reed-Solomon (RS) codes

Sequential decoding, with convolutional
    codes, 85–86
Shannon's theorem, 8–10
Soft-decision decoding, 5–7
    with convolutional codes, 84–85
Sources, correlated, 102–7
Sphere-packing, 7–8
Standard array, 12
Subspace, 12
Syndrome, 15–17
Syndrome decoding, with convolutional
    codes, 87–91

Tree codes, 69–72
Trellis codes, 69–72

Varsharmov-Gilbert bound, 19–20
Viterbi algorithm, 70–72

Weight, of linear code, 17
Weight distributions
    of cyclic codes, 39–40
    of Reed-Solomon code, 64–65

The Artech House Telecommunications Library

Vinton G. Cerf, Series Editor

Advanced Technology for Road Transport: IVHS and ATT, Ian Catling, editor

Advances in Computer Communications and Networking, Wesley W. Chu, editor

Advances in Computer Systems Security, Rein Turn, editor

Analysis and Synthesis of Logic Systems, Daniel Mange

Asynchronous Transfer Mode Networks: Performance Issues, Raif O. Onvural

A Bibliography of Telecommunications and Socio-Economic Development, Heather E. Hudson

Broadband: Business Services, Technologies, and Strategic Impact, David Wright

Broadband Network Analysis and Design, Daniel Minoli

Broadband Telecommunications Technology, Byeong Lee, Minho Kang, and Jonghee Lee

Cellular Radio: Analog and Digital Systems, Asha Mehrotra

Cellular Radio Systems, D. M. Balston and R. C. V. Macario, editors

Client/Server Computing: Architecture, Applications, and Distributed Systems Management, Bruce Elbert and Bobby Martyna

Codes for Error Control and Synchronization, Djimitri Wiggert

Communication Satellites in the Geostationary Orbit, Donald M. Jansky and Michel C. Jeruchim

Communications Directory, Manus Egan, editor

The Complete Guide to Buying a Telephone System, Paul Daubitz

Computer Telephone Integration, Rob Walters

The Corporate Cabling Guide, Mark W. McElroy

Corporate Networks: The Strategic Use of Telecommunications, Thomas Valovic

Current Advances in LANs, MANs, and ISDN, B. G. Kim, editor

Design and Prospects for the ISDN, G. Dicenet

Digital Cellular Radio, George Calhoun

Digital Hardware Testing: Transistor-Level Fault Modeling and Testing, Rochit Rajsuman, editor

Digital Signal Processing, Murat Kunt

Digital Switching Control Architectures, Giuseppe Fantauzzi

Digital Transmission Design and Jitter Analysis, Yoshitaka Takasaki

Distributed Multimedia Through Broadband Communications Services, Daniel Minoli and Robert Keinath

Distributed Processing Systems, Volume I, Wesley W. Chu, editor

Disaster Recovery Planning for Telecommunications, Leo A. Wrobel

Document Imaging Systems: Technology and Applications, Nathan J. Muller

EDI Security, Control, and Audit, Albert J. Marcella and Sally Chen

Enterprise Networking: Fractional T1 to SONET, Frame Relay to BISDN, Daniel Minoli

Expert Systems Applications in Integrated Network Management, E. C. Ericson, L. T. Ericson, and D. Minoli, editors

FAX: Digital Facsimile Technology and Applications, Second Edition, Dennis Bodson, Kenneth McConnell, and Richard Schaphorst

FDDI and FDDI-II: Architecture, Protocols, and Performance, Bernhard Albert and Anura P. Jayasumana

Fiber Network Service Survivability, Tsong-Ho Wu

Fiber Optics and CATV Business Strategy, Robert K. Yates *et al.*

A Guide to Fractional T1, J. E. Trulove

A Guide to the TCP/IP Protocol Suite, Floyd Wilder

Implementing EDI, Mike Hendry

Implementing X.400 and X.500: The PP and QUIPU Systems, Steve Kille

Inbound Call Centers: Design, Implementation, and Management, Robert A. Gable

Information Superhighways: The Economics of Advanced Public Communication Networks, Bruce Egan

Integrated Broadband Networks, Amit Bhargava

Integrated Services Digital Networks, Anthony M. Rutkowski

Intelcom '94: The Outlook for Mediterranean Communications, Stephen McClelland, editor

International Telecommunications Management, Bruce R. Elbert

International Telecommunication Standards Organizations, Andrew Macpherson

Internetworking LANs: Operation, Design, and Management, Robert Davidson and Nathan Muller

Introduction to Error-Correcting Codes, Michael Purser

Introduction to Satellite Communication, Bruce R. Elbert

Introduction to T1/T3 Networking, Regis J. (Bud) Bates

Introduction to Telecommunication Electronics, A. Michael Noll

Introduction to Telephones and Telephone Systems, Second Edition, A. Michael Noll

Introduction to X.400, Cemil Betanov

The ITU in a Changing World, George A. Codding, Jr. and Anthony M. Rutkowski

Jitter in Digital Transmission Systems, Patrick R. Trischitta and Eve L. Varma

Land-Mobile Radio System Engineering, Garry C. Hess

LAN/WAN Optimization Techniques, Harrell Van Norman

LANs to WANs: Network Management in the 1990s, Nathan J. Muller and Robert P. Davidson

The Law and Regulation of International Space Communication, Harold M. White, Jr. and Rita Lauria White

Long Distance Services: A Buyer's Guide, Daniel D. Briere

Measurement of Optical Fibers and Devices, G. Cancellieri and U. Ravaioli

Meteor Burst Communication, Jacob Z. Schanker

Minimum Risk Strategy for Acquiring Communications Equipment and Services, Nathan J. Muller

Mobile Communications in the U.S. and Europe: Regulation, Technology, and Markets, Michael Paetsch

Mobile Information Systems, John Walker

Narrowband Land-Mobile Radio Networks, Jean-Paul Linnartz

Networking Strategies for Information Technology, Bruce Elbert

Numerical Analysis of Linear Networks and Systems, Hermann Kremer *et al.*

Optimization of Digital Transmission Systems, K. Trondle and Gunter Soder

Packet Switching Evolution from Narrowband to Broadband ISDN, M. Smouts

Packet Video: Modeling and Signal Processing, Naohisa Ohta

The PP and QUIPU Implementation of X.400 and X.500, Stephen Kille

Principles of Secure Communication Systems, Second Edition, Don J. Torrieri

Principles of Signals and Systems: Deterministic Signals, B. Picinbono

Private Telecommunication Networks, Bruce Elbert

Radio-Relay Systems, Anton A. Huurdeman

Radiodetermination Satellite Services and Standards, Martin Rothblatt

Residential Fiber Optic Networks: An Engineering and Economic Analysis, David Reed

Secure Data Networking, Michael Purser

Setting Global Telecommunication Standards: The Stakes, The Players, and The Process, Gerd Wallenstein

Smart Cards, José Manuel Otón and José Luis Zoreda

The Telecommunications Deregulation Sourcebook, Stuart N. Brotman, editor

Television Technology: Fundamentals and Future Prospects, A. Michael Noll

Telecommunications Technology Handbook, Daniel Minoli

Telephone Company and Cable Television Competition, Stuart N. Brotman

Teletraffic Technologies in ATM Networks, Hiroshi Saito

Terrestrial Digital Microwave Communciations, Ferdo Ivanek, editor

Transmission Networking: SONET and the SDH, Mike Sexton and Andy Reid

Transmission Performance of Evolving Telecommunications Networks, John Gruber and Godfrey Williams

Troposcatter Radio Links, G. Roda

UNIX Internetworking, Uday O. Pabrai

Virtual Networks: A Buyer's Guide, Daniel D. Briere

Voice Processing, Second Edition, Walt Tetschner

Voice Teletraffic System Engineering, James R. Boucher

Wireless Access and the Local Telephone Network, George Calhoun

Wireless Data Networking, Nathan J. Muller

Wireless LAN Systems, A. Santamaría and F. J. Lopez-Hernandez

Writing Disaster Recovery Plans for Telecommunications Networks and LANs, Leo A. Wrobel

X Window System User's Guide, Uday O. Pabrai

For further information on these and other Artech House titles, contact:

Artech House
685 Canton Street
Norwood, MA 02062
617-769-9750
Fax: 617-769-6334
Telex: 951-659
email: artech@world.std.com

Artech House
Portland House, Stag Place
London SW1E 5XA England
+44 (0) 71-973-8077
Fax: +44 (0) 71-630-0166
Telex: 951-659
email: bookco@artech.demon.co.uk